Glencoe
Literature
Reading with Purpose

Leveled Vocabulary Development

English Language Learners
Course 3

Glencoe

New York, New York   Columbus, Ohio   Chicago, Illinois   Peoria, Illinois   Woodland Hills, California

Glencoe

Send all inquiries to:
Glencoe/McGraw-Hill
8787 Orion Place
Columbus, OH 43240-4027

ISBN-13: 978-0-07-876509-4

ISBN-10: 0-07-876509-9

Printed in the United States of America.

1 2 3 4 5 6 7 8 9 047 12 11 10 09 08 07 06

Table of Contents

Lessons 1–10

Selection Vocabulary Practice

Ice (page 18)

Vocabulary

minority *n.* the smaller group
trait *n.* a personal quality
flaw *n.* a quality that makes something less valuable; a defect
self-esteem *n.* confidence and satisfaction in oneself
oblivious *adj.* not aware
relentlessly *adv.* without stopping; without giving up
persisted *v.* kept doing something even when it was difficult
spectator *n.* someone who watches
void *n.* empty space
elusive *adj.* hard to catch or find

Exercise A: True or False?

Circle **T** for each true statement and **F** for each false statement.

1. If a television had a *flaw*, you would probably pay more for it. **T   F**

2. Jodie has high *self-esteem*, so she likes herself just the way she is. **T   F**

3. A *spectator* at a football game usually wears a uniform. **T   F**

4. A *void* in a conversation means that no one is talking at the time. **T   F**

5. Someone who works *relentlessly* likes to fool around a lot. **T   F**

Exercise B: Context Clues

Circle the words in the sentence that help you figure out the meaning of each vocabulary word.

1. Michelle's kindness is a fine *trait*, and this characteristic will help her to be successful.

2. The *elusive* burglar slipped through the detective's hands time and again.

3. Only a small *minority* of people thought the skate park was a bad idea.

4. Austin stubbornly *persisted* with the crossword puzzle until it was done.

5. The mother was *oblivious* and did not notice her wandering child.

Name _____ Class _____ Date _____

Selection Vocabulary Practice

On Top of the World (page 32)

Vocabulary

glimpse *n.* a brief, quick look

feat *n.* difficult task; something that is very hard to do

colleagues *n.* people you work with who are your equals

summit *n.* the highest point of a mountain

irresistible *adj.* too tempting to ignore or fight against

crevasses *n.* deep cracks

scramble *v.* to move quickly and in a great hurry

conquer *v.* to win a victory over; defeat

trekked *v.* walked or hiked a long distance

expeditions *n.* groups that take trips for specific purposes

Exercise A: Words in Context

Read the paragraph. Circle the best word to complete each sentence.

My *colleagues* and I caught only a *glimpse* of the animal at the *summit* of the hill before it began to *scramble* down the other side. The urge to follow the mysterious creature was *irresistible*.

1. The speaker is on a trip with his (friends, coworkers).

2. The group watched the animal for a (long, short) time.

3. The animal stopped at the (top, bottom) of the hill.

4. The animal moved away (slowly, quickly).

5. The speaker (did, did not) want to follow the animal.

Exercise B: Answer the Questions

Choose the best answer for each question.

1. If an athlete achieved a *feat*, would he or she be proud or ashamed? _____

2. If campers *trekked* to a river, did they drive or walk there? _____

3. If a glacier had many *crevasses*, would it be safe or dangerous to climb? _____

4. If someone goes on *expeditions*, does she travel or work in a lab? _____

5. If a tennis player wants to *conquer* another player, does he want to win or help the other player win? _____

Selection Vocabulary Practice

The Tell-Tale Heart Part A (page 46)

Vocabulary

acute *adj.* sharp; highly sensitive
proceeded *v.* went forward with an action
foresight *n.* care or preparation for the future
cautious *adj.* careful
stifled *adj.* held back; muffled
distracted *v.* made unable to think clearly; confused
stimulates *v.* makes active or more active
detected *v.* noticed someone or something
audacity *n.* boldness; daring; reckless courage
hypocritical *adj.* fake; pretending to be something one isn't

Exercise A: Word Groups

Cross out the word that does not belong in each group.

1. cautious   alert   watchful   bored
2. missed   detected   saw   noticed
3. bravery   audacity   shyness   courage
4. energizes   encourages   discourages   stimulates
5. phony   real   hypocritical   imitation

Exercise B: Context Clues

Circle **C** for each correct statement and **I** for each incorrect statement.

1. The TV *distracted* Megan from her homework. **C I**

2. Some older people have such *acute* hearing that they use a hearing aid. **C I**

3. Showing great *foresight*, Al put a spare tire in the trunk in case his car got a flat. **C I**

4. Her *stifled* sneeze made a loud noise. **C I**

5. The light turned green, so the cars *proceeded* through the intersection. **C I**

Name _____ Class _____ Date _____

Selection Vocabulary Practice

The Tell-Tale Heart   Part B   (page 46)

Vocabulary

sufficient *adj.* enough
thrust *v.* to push with sudden force
hearty *adj.* cheerful; full of health and strength
inquiring *v.* asking
triumph *n.* success
awe *n.* amazement
pitied *v.* felt sorry for
stalked *v.* hunted
resolved *v.* made a firm decision
ceased *v.* stopped

Exercise: Crossword Puzzle

Use the clues to solve the puzzle.

DOWN

2. wanting an answer
3. had sympathy for
4. tracked
5. shove
7. halted

ACROSS

1. achievement
4. as much as is needed
6. wonder; astonishment
8. happy; joyful
9. decided

Leveled Vocabulary Development, ELL

Selection Vocabulary Practice

from The Book of Rock Stars   (page 56)

Vocabulary

pursue *v.* to go after; chase

oppressed *adj.* held down; held back; kept from making progress

hypnotic *adj.* in a way that holds the complete attention of someone

rebel *v.* to stand up against

premature *adj.* early; before the right time

designated *v.* picked; chose

compassion *n.* the feeling of sorrow or pity caused by someone else's misfortunes; sympathy

converted *v.* changed

devotion *n.* complete loyalty

comeback *n.* a return to a former position or condition

Exercise A: Context Clues

Circle the words in the sentence that help you figure out the meaning of each vocabulary word.

1. Samantha was *designated* leader. She was chosen over other girls.

2. Kids may *rebel* and fight against efforts to make them behave.

3. Dan was known for *compassion*. He had great concern for others.

4. It is important to *pursue* your goals—to chase after your dreams.

5. The *oppressed* villagers were not able to improve their lives.

Exercise B: Words in Context

Choose the best word from the list to complete each sentence below.

1. A fan of a movie star might show his _____ by writing a fan letter.

2. The band *Green Day* made a _____ with its new hit song.

3. Television can be _____ because it attracts and keeps your attention.

4. Her baby sister was _____ because she was born too early.

5. Carrie and Sam _____ the gym into a dance hall for the prom.

Selection Vocabulary Practice

The March of the Mill Children (page 66)

Vocabulary

treacherous *adj.* dangerous; not reliable; not trustworthy
publicity *n.* attention; advertising
mutilated *adj.* damaged in a way that cannot be repaired
hesitated *v.* waited before doing something
grumbled *v.* complained
dormitory *n.* a building with rooms for people to sleep in
swarms *n.* large groups or crowds
weary *adj.* very tired
solemnly *adv.* seriously
grueling *adj.* difficult; exhausting

Exercise A: This or That?

Choose the best answer for each question.

1. How would you break news *solemnly*, by laughing or talking quietly? _____

2. If an actress wants *publicity*, will she talk to or hide from reporters? _____

3. Which insects travel in *swarms*, earthworms or mosquitoes? _____

4. If the ice on a lake is *treacherous*, should you stay off or walk on it? _____

5. How would you feel after a *grueling* hike, full of energy or very tired? _____

6. If a painting has been *mutilated*, is it in good shape or ruined? _____

Exercise B: Words in Context

Choose the best word from the list to complete each sentence below.

1. Nina, hot and _____, finally made it to the top of the mountain.

2. Not knowing what to say, Carl _____ before speaking.

3. Liz and Xia _____ to each other because they needed to redo their homework.

4. The students rushed to exit their _____ for the fire drill.

Selection Vocabulary Practice

Filling Out the Application *and* Exploring Careers   (page 78)

Vocabulary

prone *adj.* likely to act or be a certain way
current *adj.* at the present time
residences *n.* places where one lives
permit *n.* document allowing one to do something
requested *v.* asked for
accurate *adj.* correct; true
replacement *n.* somebody or something that takes the place of another
dependable *adj.* able to be relied upon
irregular *adj.* not happening at evenly spaced times
revive *v.* to bring back to life or to good health

Exercise A: Mystery Word

Choose the best word from the list to complete each sentence.
Unscramble the circled letters to discover the mystery word.

1. Chris needed a ◯_ _ _ _ _ ◯_ _ _ part to fix his bike.

2. The weather report is usually _ _ _ _ _ _ ◯_ .

3. Kim worked an ◯_ _ _ _ _ _ _ _ _ schedule at the store.

4. Brandon was ◯_ _ _ _ to having accidents.

5. The _ _ _ _ ◯_ _ mayor is more popular than the last one.

Mystery Word _ _ _ _ _ _ _

Exercise B: Words in Context

Read the paragraph and circle the best word to complete each sentence.

1. DR. BROWN: I see you (requested, replacement) Saturdays off.

2. ANDREA: Yes, I visit seniors at their (permit, residences).

3. DR. BROWN: We are looking for someone (dependable, prone).

   ANDREA: You can rely on me! I always show up on time.

   DR. BROWN: Do you have any experience caring for animals?

4. ANDREA: Well, once I had to (requested, revive) my pet mouse after he fell into my aquarium!

Selection Vocabulary Practice

from Akiko in the Forbidden Foothills
of Gozmaturk   (page 100)

Vocabulary

unarmed *adj.* without weapons

entertaining *adj.* fun; amusing

heavenly *adj.* very wonderful, delicious, or beautiful

lullaby *n.* a song sung to make someone fall asleep

wretched *adj.* very unfortunate or unhappy; terrible

coordinate *v.* to make things work together smoothly

Exercise A: Words in Context

Choose the best word from the list to complete each sentence below.

1. The _____ thief slowly opened the bank's front door,
raising his arms above his head and giving up.

2. Katie sang her little sister a _____ to help her fall back asleep.

3. The baking cookies smelled _____ when Felix opened
the oven.

4. Sandra was exhausted from dealing with several mean and
_____ customers.

5. It was difficult for Tim's parents to _____ their schedules
because they each worked different hours.

Exercise B: Synonyms or Antonyms?

Write **S** if the words are synonyms. Write **A** if they are antonyms.

____ **1.** coordinate, organize

____ **2.** wretched, wonderful

____ **3.** unarmed, defenseless

____ **4.** entertaining, boring

____ **5.** heavenly, delightful

Selection Vocabulary Practice

Being Japanese American   (page 108)

Vocabulary

superstitions *n.* beliefs not based on facts
object *v.* to feel strongly against or opposed to something
corresponded *v.* wrote letters to one another
relish *n.* enjoyment or delight
astonished *adj.* amazed
customary *adj.* the way things are usually done
humiliated *adj.* embarrassed; ashamed
branch *n.* a separate office building associated with a main building
treasured *v.* valued highly
festive *adj.* cheerful; suitable for a party or festival

Exercise A: Matching

Write the letter of the ending that matches the beginning of each sentence.

___ **1.** Balloons made the living room   **A.** old *superstitions*.

___ **2.** Leaving a tip at a restaurant is   **B.** great *relish*.

___ **3.** As the volcano erupted, he felt   **C.** very *festive*.

___ **4.** Justin ate the last cupcake with   **D.** a *customary* practice.

___ **5.** Black cats play a role in many   **E.** quite *astonished*.

Exercise B: Analogies

Choose the best word from the list to complete the analogy.

1. To go along with IS TO agree AS to argue against IS TO _____.

2. Had a conversation IS TO made a phone call AS wrote a letter
IS TO _____.

3. Threw away IS TO hated AS kept forever IS TO _____.

4. Treated with respect IS TO proud AS treated with disrespect IS TO _____.

5. Pie IS TO slice AS central bank IS TO _____.

Name _____ Class _____ Date _____

Selection Vocabulary Practice
from A Gift of Laughter   (page 119)

Vocabulary

bounded *v.* moved quickly with great energy
appealed *v.* made a serious request
bewilderment *n.* confusion
rage *n.* great anger
contributor *n.* someone who gives or donates to help
worthy *adj.* important and valuable enough to fulfill a purpose
shuddering *n.* shaking; trembling
staccato *adj.* quick, short, abrupt
magnificent *adj.* very beautiful and impressive
superiority *n.* a feeling of being better than someone else

Exercise A: Synonyms
Write the vocabulary word that is the synonym for the underlined word.

1. The dog <u>ran</u> up the driveway and into the house. _____

2. Suzie <u>asked</u> for her grandfather's help with her history homework. _____

3. Freddy looked around at the surprise party in <u>uncertainty</u> because he had no idea it was for him. _____

4. Jacinta was full of <u>anger</u> after finding out that Diego ran over her bike. _____

5. Akilah's father is a <u>donor</u> who gives money to the local hospital. _____

Exercise B: Words in Context
Choose the best word from the list to complete each sentence below.

1. Alaska is known for its _____ glaciers and mountain ranges.

2. The track team showed its _____ by winning first place.

3. Once Brian calmed down, he stopped _____.

4. Sara finally found a gift _____ of her parents' anniversary.

5. The _____ sound of firecrackers filled the air.

Selection Vocabulary Practice

A Family Thing *and* Knoxville, Tennessee
(page 124)

Vocabulary

procedure *n.* a series of steps taken to do something
recollections *n.* memories
constant *adj.* happening again and again
gloomy *adj.* sad; depressed
labored *v.* worked
device *n.* a tool or machine
seasoned *adj.* experienced
eclipsed *v.* made to seem unimportant
inevitable *adj.* certain to happen; unavoidable
wobbling *v.* moving in a swaying, shaking, or unsteady way

Exercise A: Words in Context

Circle the letter of the best word to complete each sentence below.

1. The newborn colt was _____ on his shaky legs.
   A. eclipsed   **B.** seasoned   **C.** wobbling

2. José's talents often _____ those of his younger brother.
   A. inevitable   **B.** constant   **C.** eclipsed

3. Anna invented a _____ that automatically butters toast.
   A. recollections   **B.** device   **C.** labored

4. Dr. Smith was a _____ surgeon, with 20 years' experience.
   A. gloomy   **B.** seasoned   **C.** wobbling

5. Grandpa Phil enjoyed sharing his _____ of his childhood.
   A. eclipsed   **B.** procedure   **C.** recollections

Exercise B: Matching

Write the letter of the definition that matches each vocabulary word.

____ 1. gloomy   **A.** worked
____ 2. constant   **B.** process
____ 3. procedure   **C.** nonstop
____ 4. labored   **D.** definite
____ 5. inevitable   **E.** unhappy

UNIT 2

Selection Vocabulary Practice

The People Could Fly (page 164)

Vocabulary

captured *v.* caught or trapped
shed *v.* dropped; got rid of
misery *n.* a state of extreme sadness
scorned *adj.* looked down upon by someone
soothe *v.* to comfort
snarled *v.* made tangled or knotted
clumsily *adv.* ungracefully; awkwardly
snag *v.* to catch hold of or tear by a sharp object
ancient *adj.* belonging to the distant past; very old
shuffle *v.* to walk slowly without lifting one's feet

Exercise A: Words in Context

Choose the best word from the list to complete each sentence below.

1. The _____ pyramid was over 5,000 years old.

2. Rafael guided his kite so that the tree branch would not _____ it.

3. Trisha danced _____, stepping all over her partner's feet.

4. Lemon tea with honey can _____ a sore throat.

5. The live trap _____ the bear that had wandered into town.

Exercise B: Matching

Write the letter of the definition that matches each vocabulary word.

___ **1.** shed   **A.** twisted up
___ **2.** misery   **B.** disrespected
___ **3.** scorned   **C.** lost
___ **4.** snarled   **D.** drag one's feet
___ **5.** shuffle   **E.** unhappiness

Selection Vocabulary Practice

A Father's Daring Trek (page 172)

Vocabulary

exile *n.* the state of living away from one's home country
perilous *adj.* very dangerous or risky
hardships *n.* extreme difficulties
persecution *n.* the condition of being caused to suffer cruelty because of your beliefs
demanding *adj.* requiring a lot of effort
frigid *adj.* very cold
sacrifice *n.* the act of giving up something that is very important
destiny *n.* a person's fate or fortune

Exercise A: Words in Context

Circle the letter of the best word to complete each sentence.

1. The king went into _____ after losing power.
   A. exile   **B.** destiny   **C.** sacrifice

2. Guadalupe's _____ was to be the first female president.
   A. destiny   **B.** exile   **C.** demanding

3. Puritans fled to the United States to escape religious _____.
   A. perilous   **B.** exile   **C.** persecution

4. Karim's _____ class required him to read a book a week.
   A. destiny   **B.** demanding   **C.** perilous

Exercise B: Antonyms

Write the vocabulary word that is the antonym for the underlined word.

1. The walk down the Grand Canyon is <u>easy</u>, and there is no danger. _____

2. The palm trees swayed back and forth in the <u>warm</u> breeze. _____

3. High school for Pippa was fun and full of <u>effortlessness</u>. _____

4. It is not a <u>gain</u> to give up chocolate if you don't even like chocolate! _____

UNIT 2

Selection Vocabulary Practice

Paul Revere's Ride (page 186)

Vocabulary

muffled *adj.* made to be quiet

stealthy *adj.* slow and secretive to avoid being seen or heard

somber *adj.* dark and gloomy

dread *n.* great fear of something about to happen

lingers *v.* waits or is slow in leaving

kindled *v.* set on fire or created interest in something

tranquil *adj.* peaceful

aghast *adj.* horrified

emerge *v.* to come out into view

defiance *n.* the act of challenging authority

Exercise A: True or False?

Circle **T** for each true statement and **F** for each false statement.

1. A *muffled* noise can make your ears ring. **T F**

2. When people are in a *somber* mood, they are fun to be around. **T F**

3. When winter *lingers*, it lasts longer than it normally does. **T F**

4. Seeing an extremely messy room can leave a parent *aghast*. **T F**

5. Two things people *dread* are summer vacation and the weekend. **T F**

Exercise B: Context Clues

Circle the words in the sentence that help you figure out the meaning of each vocabulary word.

1. The *tranquil* forest was quiet and peaceful.

2. The disrespectful girl ran away from her mother in *defiance*.

3. The lightning *kindled* the dry grass and started the prairie fire.

4. The last chick to *emerge* from its shell came out into the world.

5. The *stealthy* thief crept slowly into the bank to rob it.

Leveled Vocabulary Development, ELL

UNIT 2

Selection Vocabulary Practice

The Oxcart (page 196)

Vocabulary

procession *n.* a group of individuals walking forward together in a ceremony

disgraced *v.* made to feel ashamed

unforeseen *adj.* something not thought of beforehand

elegant *adj.* beautiful and tasteful

stench *n.* a strong and very unpleasant smell

lurching *adj.* rolling or swaying in a jerky motion

horrid *adj.* awful; terrible

distinguished *adj.* well-known for excellence and honor

Exercise A: Words in Context

Read the paragraph. Circle the best word or phrase to complete each sentence.

The *procession* of graduating seniors walked onto the football field and took their seats. As the mayor began her speech, a tiny skunk climbed the stairs to the podium. *Lurching* up from their seats, the *distinguished* guests held their noses as a *stench* filled the air.

1. The graduating seniors entered the field (one by one, as a big group).

2. The guests rose from their seats in a (jerking, smooth) motion.

3. The guests were (parents, important people) from the community.

4. Suddenly, (a bad smell, a loud noise) filled the air.

Exercise B: If . . . ?

Choose the best answer for each question.

1. If a hotel is *elegant*, is it ugly or beautiful? _____

2. If a family feels *disgraced*, do they feel ashamed or proud? _____

3. If a child has *horrid* manners, is he nice to other people or rude? _____

4. If a problem was *unforeseen*, was it a surprise or an expected event? _____

UNIT 2

Selection Vocabulary Practice

The Snake Chief   (page 208)

UNIT 2

Vocabulary

contentedly *adv.* in a satisfied way; happily
headstrong *adj.* stubborn
induce *v.* to convince to do something; influence
quavered *v.* spoke in a shaky or trembling voice
boast *v.* to brag
incompetence *n.* lack of ability or skill
reluctantly *adv.* against one's will
courteously *adv.* politely
prospered *v.* had success, wealth, and good fortune

Exercise A: Context Clues

Circle the word or phrase in the sentence that helps you figure out the meaning of each vocabulary word.

1. Jodie tried to *induce* Nick to go but failed to persuade him.

2. The brothers *prospered*, becoming rich off their invention.

3. Known for being *headstrong*, mules are smart but stubborn animals.

4. Travis waxed his car *contentedly*, polishing it happily.

Exercise B: Complete the Sentence

Choose the best word from the list to complete each sentence below.

1. Students often _____ about good grades.

2. A professional football player could show _____ by losing a game.

3. Su can't swim, so she _____ entered the pool.

4. Students acted _____ by paying attention in class.

5. Timmy, a new student, _____ when meeting new people.

6. No amount of money could _____ me to go skydiving.

Selection Vocabulary Practice

from Harriet Tubman: Conductor on the Underground Railroad   Part A   (page 220)

Vocabulary

intervals *n.* spaces of time between one event and another

forbidden *adj.* not allowed

hastily *adv.* in a hurried way

vivid *adj.* able to create clear pictures in one's mind

incentive *n.* a reward used to get people to act

eloquence *n.* the ability to speak clearly and powerfully

disclose *v.* to make known; reveal

cajoling *v.* persuading

Exercise A: Word Groups

Cross out the word that does not belong in each group.

1. banned   illegal   forbidden   allowed

2. show   display   hide   disclose

3. cajoling   encouraging   warning   influencing

4. prize   bonus   incentive   punishment

5. slowly   hastily   quickly   speedily

Exercise B: True or False?

Circle **T** for each true statement and **F** for each false statement.

1. The teacher's description of Africa was so *vivid*, that Alyssa could almost see the grains of sand in the desert. **T   F**

2. There was no relief from the nonstop pain that came in *intervals*. **T   F**

3. Kaitlin spoke with *eloquence*, mispronouncing half the words of her speech. **T   F**

UNIT 2

Selection Vocabulary Practice

from Harriet Tubman: Conductor on the Underground Railroad   Part B   (page 220)

Vocabulary

indicate *v.* to show
invariably *adv.* every time; without fail
fugitives *n.* people running away from something
vicinity *n.* the area close by
disheveled *adj.* messy
suspicious *adj.* not trusting
defeated *v.* beaten; crushed
whence *adv.* from where

Exercise: Crack the Code

Choose the best word from the list to match each clue. Use the numbers to solve the password.

1. untidy; sloppy ___ ___ ___ ___ ___ ___ ___ ___ ___ ___
4 9 19 8 5 22 5 12 5 4

2. crushed in battle ___ ___ ___ ___ ___ ___ ___ ___
4 5 6 5 1 20 5 4

3. neighborhood ___ ___ ___ ___ ___ ___ ___ ___
22 9 3 9 14 9 20 25

4. escaped people ___ ___ ___ ___ ___ ___ ___ ___ ___
6 21 7 9 20 9 22 5 19

5. point out ___ ___ ___ ___ ___ ___ ___ ___
9 14 4 9 3 1 20 5

6. from what place ___ ___ ___ ___ ___ ___
23 8 5 14 3 5

7. always ___ ___ ___ ___ ___ ___ ___ ___ ___ ___
9 14 22 1 18 9 1 2 12 25

8. unbelieving ___ ___ ___ ___ ___ ___ ___ ___ ___ ___
19 21 19 16 9 3 9 15 21 19

PASSWORD: " ___ ___ ___ ___ ___ ___ ___
1 6 18 9 5 14 4

___ ___ ___ ___ ___ ___ ___ ___ ___ ___ ___."
23 9 20 8 6 18 9 5 14 4 19

Selection Vocabulary Practice

Icarus and Daedalus (page 242)

Vocabulary

cunning *adj.* clever; tricky
veered *v.* suddenly changed direction
captive *adj.* trapped; held prisoner
wavered *v.* became unsteady
rash *adj.* reckless; done without thought or concern
cautions *n.* warnings
remained *v.* stayed
vacancy *n.* an empty or unoccupied space
quench *v.* to satisfy a need
offering *n.* a gift or donation

Exercise A: Mystery Word

Choose the best word from the list to complete each sentence.
Unscramble the circled letters to discover the mystery word.

1. The pirates held the captain __ __ __◯__ __ __ for a month.

2. Think carefully to avoid making a __◯◯__ decision.

3. To make up, Ed gave Ann flowers as a peace◯__ __ __ __◯__ __.

4. A frosty glass of iced tea will __ __ __◯__ __ your thirst.

5. The __◯__ __ __ __ __ thief left no fingerprints behind.

6. All the applicants for the __ __ __ __ __◯__ were well qualified.

Mystery word __ __ __ __ __ __ __ __ __

Exercise B: Complete the Conversation

Read the conversation. Circle the best word to complete each sentence.

1. ICARUS: Dad, you should have seen me when I (veered, remained) around that seagull!

2. DAEDALUS: I was (captive, rash) to allow you to use those wings!

3. ICARUS: I (wavered, quench) a bit, then dodged to the right!

4. DAEDALUS: If only we could have (vacancy, remained) in Crete!

5. ICARUS: Then I dove low and sipped seawater to (quench, veered) my thirst! It was awesome!

UNIT 2

Selection Vocabulary Practice

A Dose of Medicine (page 250)

Vocabulary

prospect *n.* a mental picture of something to come
administered *v.* gave
hilarious *adj.* very funny
deaden *v.* to make weak or dull
eager *adj.* very willing; enthusiastic
extracted *v.* took out using force
consciousness *n.* the state of being fully awake or alert
publicized *v.* made the public aware of something
stagger *v.* to walk unsteadily; stumble
collapsed *v.* fell suddenly

Exercise A: This or That?

Choose the best answer for each question.

1. If a job is a likely *prospect*, is it a job someone had or might have? _____

2. How would you *deaden* the sound of a CD, by turning it up or down? _____

3. When someone loses *consciousness*, is he or she asleep or awake? _____

4. When a movie is *publicized*, is it talked about or kept secret? _____

5. If a doctor *administered* a shot, did she order the shot or give the shot? _____

Exercise B: Words in Context

Choose the best word from the list to complete each sentence below.

1. When James is really tired he will often _____ up the stairs to his room.

2. Erica _____ on the couch after a long day of classes.

3. Maria's mom carefully _____ the burnt and broken piece of bread from the toaster.

4. The entire class was _____ to help organize the event.

5. Max's best friend is the class clown because he is so _____.

Selection Vocabulary Practice

Kamau's Finish   (page 259)

UNIT 2

Vocabulary

crouch *v.* to get down close to the ground by bending the legs
scold *v.* to speak to someone angrily
financial *adj.* concerning money
distracted *adj.* losing attention easily
prodded *v.* poked
destination *n.* the place one is going to
jolts *v.* moves with a sudden, hard blow
dramatic *adj.* showing strong emotion
beaming *v.* smiling with great happiness
sheepishly *adv.* with embarrassment

Exercise A: Words in Context

Choose the best word from the list to complete each sentence below.

1. Kim _____ Tia in order to get her attention because she was _____.

2. I know my mother will _____ me because I never pay attention to her _____ advice, and I always owe her money.

3. Chen decided to _____ behind the bushes so he could eavesdrop on his sister, but after she caught him all he could do was smile _____.

4. Kirk's _____ final lines in the play left him _____ and very happy.

5. Ayita cannot wait to reach their _____ because the car _____ so much.

Exercise B: Synonyms or Antonyms?

Write **S** if the words are synonyms. Write **A** if they are antonyms.
___ **1.** beaming   crying
___ **2.** scold   praise
___ **3.** crouch   bend

UNIT 2

Selection Vocabulary Practice

The Bunion Derby (page 268)

Vocabulary

mortgage *n.* a loan to buy a house or other property
furnished *v.* supplied; given
belongings *n.* things one owns
promoter *n.* a person who organizes and pays the costs of a sporting event
grimacing *v.* making a face that shows discomfort or disgust
doggedly *adv.* with great determination
consecutive *adj.* one after the other
notable *adj.* outstanding; remarkable

Exercise A: Matching

Write the letter of the ending that matches the beginning of each sentence.

_____**1.** The Smiths finished buying their home

_____**2.** Ruthie lost all of her

_____**3.** Climbing Mount Everest is

_____**4.** The manager paid a fee to

A. a *notable* achievement.

B. by paying off their *mortgage*.

C. the boxing *promoter*.

D. *belongings* in the flood.

Exercise B: Answer the Questions

Choose the best word from the choices below to answer each question.

grimacing   *doggedly*   *consecutive*   *furnished*

1. Which word tells that a school provided its students with supplies? _____

2. Which word tells how someone pursued a goal? _____

3. Which word describes a look on a person's face? _____

4. Which word talks about the order in which things happen? _____

Selection Vocabulary Practice

Gymnasts in Pain: Out of Balance   Part A   (page 300)

Vocabulary

pressured *v.* forced into doing something
expectations *n.* outcomes considered likely to happen
maneuvers *n.* clever or skillful moves or actions
obsession *n.* something that one thinks of constantly
smuggled *v.* brought something in secretly
downplayed *v.* lessened the importance or seriousness of something
fragile *n.* easy to break
elite *adj.* the best or most talented
scorn *n.* anger, ridicule, or disrespect
decades *n.* periods of ten years

Exercise A: Context Clues

Circle the words in the sentence that help you figure out the meaning of each vocabulary word.

1. Erin *smuggled* the puppy in by sneaking it through the kitchen door.

2. The *elite* orchestra featured the top musicians of the country.

3. The skateboarders were very skilled and could do many different *maneuvers*.

4. Cara's parents felt her passion for singing was a healthy *obsession*.

5. Sam's dad *pressured* him to do well at school, pushing harder every day.

Exercise B: Words in Context

Choose the best word from the list to complete each sentence below.

1. Kimmy _____ her injury because she wanted to play the tennis match.

2. A box would be labeled _____ if it had glassware in it.

3. Tony felt _____ for the people who harm animals.

4. A lot of people have high _____ for themselves.

5. An employee who has worked for one _____, has worked for ten years.

UNIT 3

Selection Vocabulary Practice

Gymnasts in Pain: Out of Balance Part B (page 300)

UNIT 3

Vocabulary

repeatedly *adv.* said, done, or occurring again and again
similar *adj.* like something else
daring *adj.* bold
acknowledged *v.* admitted
fractured *adj.* broken
recalled *v.* remembered
consuming *v.* eating
verbal *adj.* of, relating to, or consisting of words
sensation *n.* feeling
inserted *v.* placed something inside

Exercise: Word Search

Read the clues and guess the corresponding vocabulary words.
Then search for the words in the puzzle.

1. physical awareness _____

2. with words _____

3. having food _____

4. put in _____

5. over and over _____

6. thought of again _____

7. brave _____

8. the same _____

9. shattered _____

10. accepted as true _____

A	O	Q	I	N	S	E	R	T	E	D	D	S
C	R	O	V	W	C	R	A	M	A	W	A	I
K	E	M	R	Q	O	A	W	V	D	V	N	M
N	P	Q	L	V	R	Q	A	B	R	L	J	I
O	E	W	V	E	R	B	A	L	E	R	S	L
W	A	J	L	M	D	R	N	A	N	A	W	A
L	T	M	C	O	N	S	U	M	I	N	G	R
E	E	R	R	N	W	D	V	A	W	L	A	D
D	D	O	F	R	A	C	T	U	R	E	D	V
G	L	R	L	A	R	A	Q	M	L	T	A	O
E	Y	W	R	E	C	A	L	L	E	D	M	R
D	N	Q	V	N	W	V	Q	R	L	R	R	M
W	S	L	M	S	E	N	S	A	T	I	O	N
N	O	R	W	M	O	N	R	V	A	L	A	A
D	A	R	I	N	G	S	L	J	M	N	R	M

Selection Vocabulary Practice

In Response to Executive Order 9066 (page 312)

Vocabulary

response *n.* something said, written, or done in answer to

executive *adj.* concerned with the administration and enforcement of laws or the affairs of government.

descent *n.* lineage; ancestry

relocation *n.* the act of moving to a new place

ripened *v.* became ready to eat

Exercise A: Words in Context

Circle the letter of the best word to complete each sentence.

1. The tomatoes _____ to a brilliant shade of red.
   A. response   **B.** relocation   **C.** ripened

2. The president made an _____ decision.
   A. descent   **B.** executive   **C.** response

3. There was no _____ when Andrea knocked on the door.
   A. response   **B.** descent   **C.** ripened

4. Mrs. Sanchez was of Spanish _____.
   A. descent   **B.** relocation   **C.** executive

5. After their _____ to Denver, the Green family learned to ski.
   A. ripened   **B.** response   **C.** relocation

Exercise B: Context Clues

Circle **C** for each correct statement and **I** for each incorrect statement.

1. Bill's family was of royal *descent*; his grandfather was a duke. **C I**

2. Lori received two phone calls in *response* to her ad in the paper. **C I**

3. The club formed an *executive* committee to decide how to spend the money from the fund-raiser. **C I**

4. The *ripened* dog was sleeping outside. **C I**

5. Everyone agreed to the airport's *relocation* from the center of town to an area outside of town. **C I**

UNIT 3

Selection Vocabulary Practice

The Games Kids Play (page 326)

UNIT 3

Vocabulary

gory *adj.* bloody; involving a lot of bloodshed
extends *v.* lengthens or stretches out
clamor *v.* to demand something in a noisy or desperate way
aggression *n.* angry, threatening, and violent behavior or actions
modified *adj.* changed; altered
portray *v.* to show or represent someone or something
offended *v.* became hurt and angry
transformed *v.* altered in shape, form, or appearance
conclusive *adj.* definite; proven without doubt
declines *v.* goes down in number

Exercise A: Mystery Word

Choose the best word from the list to match each clue. Unscramble the circled letters to discover the mystery vocabulary word.

1. altered __ __ __ __ __ __(__)

2. something is changed __ __ __ __(__)__ __ __ __(__)__

3. angry behavior __ __ __(__)__ __(__)__(__)

4. to make an uproar (__)(__)__ __ __ __

Mystery word __ __ __ __ __ __ __ __

Exercise B: Synonyms or Antonyms?

Write **S** if the words are synonyms. Write **A** if they are antonyms.

___ **1.** offended, insulted
___ **2.** clamor, reject
___ **3.** portray, present
___ **4.** declines, increases
___ **5.** transformed, altered
___ **6.** conclusive, certain
___ **7.** modified, unchanged
___ **8.** extends, increases

Copyright © by The McGraw-Hill Companies, Inc.

Leveled Vocabulary Development, ELL

Selection Vocabulary Practice

Cruise Control   (page 332)

Vocabulary

restrictions *n.* limits to things you can and can't do
beloved *adj.* dearly loved
humiliating *adj.* embarrassing to someone's pride
notify *v.* to give notice; to inform
banners *n.* signs
perceives *v.* to become aware of through the senses, especially sight; understand

Exercise A: Words in Context

Choose the best word from the list to complete each sentence.

1. Alexis cried for days when her _____ hamster died.

2. It was _____ for George to ride his sister's pink bicycle.

3. The bright _____ announced that the circus was coming to town.

4. Carmen's mother placed _____ on her use of the phone.

5. The neighbors called to _____ Joe that his dog was loose.

Exercise B: Synonyms

Write the vocabulary word that is the synonym for the underlined word.

1. Students often have <u>limitations</u> placed on them. _____

2. Talia and Miguel put up huge <u>posters</u> on the front door and in the kitchen for their sister's 16th birthday. _____

3. The cat's <u>favorite</u> toy is a mouse that squeaks. _____

4. Kiran always <u>sees</u> things differently than I do. _____

5. It was very <u>embarrassing</u> to lose our first home basketball game to the worst team in the state. _____

Exercise C: Responding to the Selection

Imagine that you design bumper stickers to make people better drivers. On a separate sheet of paper, write three bumper stickers and make sure to use at least three of the vocabulary words.

UNIT 3

Selection Vocabulary Practice

Flowers for Algernon, Part 2   Part A   (page 358)

UNIT 3

Vocabulary

glory *n.* praise or honor
related *v.* had something to do with
acquire *v.* to get
tangible *adj.* able to be seen, touched, or felt
invariably *adv.* constantly; always
cowered *v.* moved away in fear
obscure *v.* to hide
stimulus *n.* something that causes a response

Exercise A: Matching

Write the letter of the definition that matches each vocabulary word.

____ **1.** acquire   **A.** fame
____ **2.** obscure   **B.** to receive
____ **3.** invariably   **C.** always
____ **4.** glory   **D.** to shrink away
____ **5.** cowered   **E.** to cover up

Exercise B: Context Clues

Circle the words in the sentence that help you figure out the meaning of each vocabulary word.

1. "It was no coincidence," the detective said, "that the monkey got sick the day bananas disappeared. These events are *related*!"

2. *Invariably*, Aunt Sylvia would tell me, "My goodness, look how big you're getting!" each and every time she visited.

3. Brianna finally had *tangible* proof that her little brother had been reading her diary when she found the pages stuck together with peanut butter.

4. The rabbits *cowered* fearfully in a corner as the fox approached them.

5. When the plant did not react to the *stimulus* of a loud beeping noise, the scientists concluded that corn cannot actually hear with its ears.

Selection Vocabulary Practice

Flowers for Algernon, Part 2   Part B   (page 358)

Vocabulary

technique *n.* method used to perform any operation or achieve a goal
accomplishing *v.* succeeding in carrying out or performing a task
toying *v.* playing with
despised *v.* hated a great deal
incident *n.* something that happened
smirking *v.* smiling in a mean way
equipped *v.* supplied with what is needed
disturbed *adj.* emotionally upset
significant *adj.* important; notable
impaired *adj.* damaged; not able to work as well as usual

Exercise: Crossword Puzzle

Use the clues to solve the puzzle.

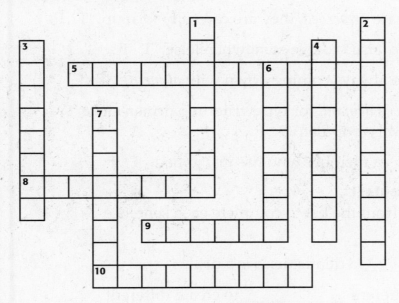

DOWN

1. broken
2. worth mentioning
3. disliked very much
4. troubled; worried
6. grinning disrespectfully
7. event

ACROSS

5. finishing
8. furnished with supplies
9. fiddling with
10. method

UNIT 3

Selection Vocabulary Practice

Tattoos: Fad, Fashion, or Folly? (page 390)

Vocabulary

practiced *v.* did something as a common routine
preserved *v.* kept in a good condition
migrated *v.* moved from one place to another
indelible *adj.* impossible to remove or erase
implements *n.* tools
ailments *n.* sicknesses
compiled *v.* collected into a book or list
initiate *n.* new member of a group or club
pigment *n.* a substance that gives colors to things
demand *n.* a need for a product or service

Exercise A: True or False?

Circle **T** for each true statement and **F** for each false statement.

1. When photographs are *preserved*, they are carefully torn up. **T   F**

2. Animals that *migrated* used to live somewhere else. **T   F**

3. Healthy children are always coming down with *ailments*. **T   F**

4. There has been a lot of *demand* for typewriter repairmen since computers became very popular. **T   F**

5. An *initiate* at a club is a member who has just joined. **T   F**

Exercise B: Words in Context

Choose the best word from the list to complete each sentence below.

1. One of the _____ a dentist uses is a drill.

2. Many artists mix different _____ to create different colors.

3. Fireworks are traditions _____ on the Fourth of July.

4. After the detective _____ all the clues, she solved the case.

5. When a shirt has an _____ stain, it is time to throw it away.

 Leveled Vocabulary Development, ELL

Selection Vocabulary Practice

Wearing Hijab: Veil of Valor (page 407)

Vocabulary

valor *n.* courage
transition *n.* a change from one thing to another
clarified *v.* made clear
emblazoned *v.* decorated with bold words or colors
immersed *v.* completely involved in something
intercede *v.* to help settle differences between others
tolerance *n.* the ability to recognize and respect different beliefs
optional *adj.* left to one's choice: not required
stellar *adj.* outstanding; terrific
camaraderie *n.* friendship within a group

Exercise A: Mystery Word

Choose the best word from the list to complete each sentence.
Unscramble the circled letters to discover the mystery word.

1. The fireman received a medal for his __ __ __(__)__ .

2. The audience applauded the actors' __(__)__(__)__ __ __ performance.

3. When her sisters fight, Cherie tries to __ __ __ __ __(__)__ __(__) .

4. The teen years mark the __ __(__)__ __ __ __ __ __(__) to adulthood.

5. The map __ __ __(__)__ __ __(__)__ the confusing directions.

Mystery word __ __ __ __ __ __ __ __ __

Exercise B: Words in Context

Read the paragraph and circle the best word to complete each
sentence.

With great *camaraderie* in their *emblazoned* uniforms, the team
wanted to shout, but Coach had no *tolerance* for rowdiness.
Immersed in silence, they heard Coach say, "Winning isn't *optional*!"

1. The uniforms were (decorated with words/spotless).

2. The coach (approved/disapproved) of rowdiness.

3. The team (stayed quiet/broke the silence).

4. Everyone on the team (disliked/liked) each other.

5. The coach believes the game is (very important/unimportant).

Selection Vocabulary Practice

from Zoya's Story   (page 414)

Vocabulary

chafed *v.* rubbed against, causing irritation
instinctively *adv.* caused by a natural response
jauntily *adv.* with cheerful self-confidence
churn *v.* to move violently
severed *adj.* chopped off
edict *n.* rule or an order
perpetrated *n.* did something
lowly *adj.* low in importance
toppled *v.* fell

Exercise A: This or That?

Choose the best answer for each question.

1. Would a shirt that *chafed* be comfortable or uncomfortable? _____

2. If a lake began to *churn*, would the water be calm or rough? _____

3. Would a worker be happy or unhappy doing a *lowly* job? _____

4. If a building *toppled* in an earthquake, did it stay up or fall down? _____

Exercise B: Words in Context

Choose the best word from the list to complete each sentence.

1. Carla _____ ducked when the football flew by her head.

2. After winning the spelling bee, Sam _____ walked out.

3. Marco _____ the carrot tops and then washed the carrots for his salad.

4. Home by 10:00 p.m. on weekends is an _____ in my house.

5. My father is working hard to find out who _____ the crime.

Selection Vocabulary Practice

Wishing Well   (page 452)

Vocabulary

mesh *n.* the weblike pattern of fibers in woven or knitted items
comforter *n.* a quilted bed covering often stuffed with feathers
flannel *n.* warm, soft fabric
minerals *n.* solid substances found in rocks
dull *adj.* faded; dark
arc *n.* a curved line between points
unconcerned *adj.* not caring

Exercise A: Words in Context

Write the best word from the list to complete each sentence.

1. The parrot was _____ that the cat was inches from its cage.

2. The miners hoped to find valuable _____ at the new site.

3. Kym pulled the _____ over her head as she tried to block
   out the sun.

4. Justin followed the _____ of the rainbow from one end to
   the other but did not find the legendary pot of gold.

5. Caught in the _____ of the web, the fly struggled helplessly.

6. Todd wore a _____ shirt to school when it was snowing.

7. The _____, tarnished teapot was obviously very old.

Exercise B: Complete the Paragraph

Choose the best words from the list to complete the paragraph.

With a deafening explosion, the rocket launched into the air,
tracing a graceful **(1)** _____ against the morning sky.
It would hopefully return to Earth with many precious
(2) _____ from the planet Xerxes. Dr. Sidney spotted a
(3) _____ metal object on the ground and bent to pick it up.
As he polished it, he had a sudden, sinking feeling. Acting
(4) _____, he asked, "Uh, is this part of the **(5)** _____
covering for the cargo hold?"

UNIT 4

Selection Vocabulary Practice

Mother to Son *and* Harlem   (page 472)

Vocabulary

splinters *n.* sharp slivers of wood
deferred *adj.* set aside or put off until a later time
fester *v.* to become infected; decay
crust *v.* to form a thin, hard layer over something soft
sags *v.* dips down; hangs low

Exercise A: Multiple Choice
Choose the letter of the best word to complete each sentence.

1. The _____ test was rescheduled for later that week.
   A. fester   **B.** deferred   **C.** sags

2. Use tweezers to get those _____ out of your fingers.
   A. crust   **B.** fester   **C.** splinters

3. As it got colder, the lake began to _____ over with ice.
   A. fester   **B.** sags   **C.** crust

4. The pony's back _____ from the weight of the kids.
   A. sags   **B.** deferred   **C.** splinters

5. The untreated wound began to _____.
   A. splinters   **B.** fester   **C.** sags

Exercise B: Context Clues
Circle **C** for each correct statement and **I** for each incorrect statement.

1. Hank wore gloves to avoid getting *splinters* from the boards. **C I**

2. The roof *sags* more every year; one day it will cave in completely. **C I**

3. The snow began to *crust*, getting soft and mushy. **C I**

4. The *deferred* audition would take place a day earlier than planned. **C I**

5. The doctor was glad to see that the injury was starting to *fester*. **C I**

Exercise C: Responding to the Selection
Langston Hughes wrote many of his poems using figurative language. On a separate sheet, write a poem that uses a simile or a metaphor. Use at least two vocabulary words.

Leveled Vocabulary Development, ELL

UNIT 4

Selection Vocabulary Practice

Sittin' on the Dock of the Bay (page 478)

Vocabulary

bay *n.* an area of the ocean surrounded by a half-circle of land
dock *n.* a platform where boats land at the edge of water
remains *v.* stays
roamed *v.* wandered; went from place to place without purpose or direction
tide *n.* the rise and fall of the ocean that occurs about every twelve hours

Exercise A: Matching

Write the letter of the ending that matches the beginning of each
sentence.

___ **1.** The girls had two hours free so they
___ **2.** Plastic in landfills never breaks down; it
___ **3.** Hundreds of shells were washed in by
___ **4.** The inexperienced boater crashed into
___ **5.** Sea storms are not quite as strong in

A. a bay.
B. the tide.
C. the dock.
D. remains forever.
E. roamed the mall.

Exercise B: Words in Context

Circle the best word to complete each sentence.

1. In a (bay, dock) you would most likely find oysters.

2. A (tide, dock) is a good place for tying up a boat.

3. If he (refrains, remains) on shore, it might be because he gets seasick.

4. If a child (roamed, remained) away on a field trip, her teacher
would probably punish her.

5. When the (tide, dock) is rising, you should probably stop
building your sand castle.

Exercise C: Responding to the Selection

On a separate sheet, write a poem about a visit to the beach.
The poem could be humorous or serious. Use at least four of the
vocabulary words.

UNIT 4

Selection Vocabulary Practice

from **To the Democratic National Convention**

(page 486)

Vocabulary

abandonment *n.* the state of being left alone without help

programmed *v.* trained to do something without thinking

carcass *n.* the dead body of a bird or animal

broadcast *n.* a television or radio program

outcast *n.* person who has been rejected by a group or by society

nomination *n.* the act of proposing a candidate for an office or honor

slum *n.* a part of a city that is in very bad condition

surrender *v.* to give up ownership or control

character *n.* the group of qualities that make up a person

qualified *adj.* having the required skills or qualities to do something

Exercise A: Context Clues

Circle the words in the sentence that help you figure out the meaning of each vocabulary word.

1. Vultures circled above the *carcass* of the deer lying on the road.

2. You can hear the radio *broadcast* of the game on FM102 at noon.

3. My *nomination* for class president is Julia Vega.

4. If you land on "bankrupt" in this game, you must *surrender* money.

5. As a doctor, Paul was *qualified* to assist the accident victims.

Exercise B: Synonyms or Antonyms?

Write **S** if the words are synonyms. Write **A** if they are antonyms.

___ **1.** abandonment, caretaking

___ **2.** programmed, taught

___ **3.** outcast, hero

___ **4.** slum, ghetto

___ **5.** character, individuality

UNIT 4

Selection Vocabulary Practice

Fable for When There's No Way Out (page 492)

Vocabulary

atmosphere *n.* the air or climate in any particular place
pecks *v.* taps sharply at
instinct *n.* unlearned knowledge that a person or animal is born with
ambition *n.* a strong drive or desire to succeed
despair *n.* a complete loss of hope
tempts *v.* causes a feeling of longing to do or have something
limp *adj.* without strength or firmness
tomb *n.* a room or chamber where a dead body is placed
stomps *v.* walks with very heavy footsteps
rage *n.* a feeling of great anger or fury

Exercise A: Words in Context

Choose the best word from the list to complete each sentence.

1. The toddler flew into a _____ whenever he had to go to bed.

2. The teacher felt _____ when the entire class failed the test.

3. Entering the ancient _____, the archeologist felt a deep sense of awe and respect.

4. Ducklings seem to know how to swim by _____.

5. It was Vanessa's lifelong _____ to live in France for a year.

Exercise B: Context Clues

Circle **C** for each correct statement and **I** for each incorrect statement.

1. The sturdy tree grew tall and *limp*. **C I**

2. Without its *atmosphere*, the Earth would not support life. **C I**

3. The kittens begin to purr when the mother cat *pecks* their heads. **C I**

4. Whenever Jason is mad, he *stomps* angrily all around the house. **C I**

5. The restaurant's all-you-can-eat buffet *tempts* everyone with its assortment of delicious foods. **C I**

UNIT 4

Selection Vocabulary Practice

O Captain! My Captain! (page 504)

Vocabulary

sought *v.* looked for
grim *adj.* gloomy; somber
bouquets *n.* flower arrangements
swaying *adj.* moving back and forth
mass *n.* a large group
anchored *adj.* held in one place with a heavy weight
victor *n.* a winner; one who defeats an opponent
mournful *adj.* filled with sadness or grief

Exercise A: Matching

Write the letter of the definition that matches each vocabulary word.

____ 1. sought
____ 2. anchored
____ 3. swaying
____ 4. mournful
____ 5. victor
____ 6. mass
____ 7. grim

A. champion
B. tried to find
C. huge crowd
D. very serious
E. leaning back and forth
F. sorrowful
G. fastened

Exercise B: Context Clues

Circle the words in the sentence that help you figure out the meaning of each vocabulary word.

1. The *bouquets* were made up of daisies and miniature roses.

2. *Anchored* down with the fifty-pound weight, the boat was going nowhere.

3. The *victor* of the tennis match shook her opponent's hand with a joyful grin.

4. With a *mournful* howl, the lonely wolf called for his missing family.

5. The *swaying* cobra moved from side to side as the snake charmer played his flute.

UNIT 4

Selection Vocabulary Practice

Scorched! How to Handle Different Types of Burns   Part A   (page 510)

Vocabulary

scorched *adj.* burnt badly

hobbled *v.* walked with difficulty; limped

smother *v.* to put out a fire by preventing it from getting air

compress *n.* a pad or cloth used to apply cold, heat, or medicine

remedies *n.* cures for illnesses

sterile *adj.* free from germs; very clean

blotchy *adj.* covered with irregular patches

pierce *v.* to prick with a sharp object

charred *adj.* burnt to the point of blackness

exposed *v.* came into contact with

Exercise A: Words in Context

Read the paragraph. Then circle the best word to complete each sentence.

Krista *hobbled* across the *charred* forest floor. The handkerchief she held to her knee as a *compress* was not at all *sterile* and she feared that the cut would become infected. Krista hoped she would be able to find the ingredients of the natural *remedies* she had learned about in camp.

1. Krista is walking (with ease, with difficulty).

2. The forest has just experienced (a flood, a fire).

3. Krista used the handkerchief to (cover a wound, gather ingredients).

4. The handkerchief is (clean, dirty).

5. Krista hopes to find ingredients to (cook a meal, heal an injury).

Exercise B: This or That?

Choose the best answer for each question.

1. If a piece of toast is *scorched*, is it overcooked or undercooked? _____

2. If a person's face is *blotchy*, is it clear or spotty? _____

3. If a sewing tool is used to *pierce* fabric, does it make a hole or sew? _____

4. If a child is *exposed* to measles, is he safe or at risk of getting sick? _____

5. If you wanted to *smother* a fire, would you use a blanket or gasoline? _____

UNIT 4

Selection Vocabulary Practice

Scorched! How to Handle Different Types of Burns   Part B   (page 510)

Vocabulary

sustaining *v.* experiencing
severity *n.* state of being very dangerous or harmful
minor *adj.* of little importance; not serious
ointment *n.* a substance used to heal
bacteria *n.* a single-celled organism that may cause disease
reduce *v.* to make less
oozing *n.* act of slowing leaking or spilling out
underlying *adj.* something that is there, but not seen at first
assistance *n.* help
resuscitation *n.* a bringing back to life or consciousness

Exercise: Crossword Puzzle

Use the clues to solve the puzzle.

ACROSS

3. seriousness

5. aid

9. beneath

10. life-saving action

DOWN

1. lessen

2. healing liquid

4. not life-threatening

6. suffering

7. dripping; trickling

8. germs

UNIT 4

Selection Vocabulary Practice

from Thura's Diary   (page 519)

Vocabulary

suburbs *n.* neighborhoods surrounding a city
freak *adj.* weird; unusual
extinguished *adj.* put out
wilt *v.* to droop; to become limp
depressed *adj.* very sad
rations *n.* portions of needed items
exact *adj.* correct and complete
precious *adj.* of great value
bombardment *n.* an attack
circumstances *n.* particular situations

Exercise A: True or False?

Circle **T** for each true statement and **F** for each false statement.

1. A house in the *suburbs* is usually located downtown. **T F**

2. An *extinguished* fire is one that has been put out. **T F**

3. A *bombardment* of snowballs happens during a snowball fight. **T F**

4. An *exact* count of students would tell about how many there are. **T F**

5. Good news always makes people feel *depressed*. **T F**

Exercise B: Words in Context

Choose the best word from the list to complete each sentence.

1. A _____ accident at the carnival surprised many people.

2. Delicate flowers will _____ when exposed to too much heat.

3. With good luck, Kory's _____ will change for the better.

4. The museum's guards watch over its _____ art collection.

5. We'll divide the _____ equally among us.

Exercise C: Responding to the Selection

Imagine that you are Thura. On a separate sheet of paper,
write an additional entry to her journal. Use at least four of the
vocabulary words.

UNIT 4

Selection Vocabulary Practice

Escaping (page 526)

Vocabulary

perseverance *n.* persistent determination
crushed *adj.* destroyed completely
stern *adj.* serious; strict
yanked *v.* pulled on strongly
glistened *v.* shone brightly
succeeded *v.* turned out as wanted; was successful
infested *adj.* filled with pests
realization *n.* a sudden awareness
imperative *adj.* extremely important; crucial
boundless *adj.* without limits

Exercise A: Word Groups

Cross out the word that does not belong in each group.

1. stubbornness	perseverance	persistence	hopelessness
2. yanked	handed over	jerked	grabbed
3. harsh	stern	firm	friendly
4. hurt	damaged	helped	crushed
5. limitless	without end	restricted	boundless
6. imperative	essential	unimportant	vital
7. failed	achieved	accomplished	succeeded
8. comprehension	realization	understanding	unawareness

Exercise B: Answer the Questions

Choose the best word from the list to answer each question.

1. If something is very important to students, what is it? _____

2. If something sparkled, what did it do? _____

3. If a team won, what did it do? _____

4. If you've just become aware of something, what have you had? _____

5. If you've found a nest of ants, what do you call that nest? _____

Selection Vocabulary Practice

Cream Puff (page 562)

Vocabulary

slunk v. walked in a quiet, secretive way to avoid attention
edge n. an advantage over another person
sneering v. smiling in a mean, nasty way
caressing v. touching softly with affection
visualizing v. creating mental images
rattled v. shaken up; made someone nervous
confirmed v. showed to be true
swaggered v. walked boldly or showed off
barreling v. running at high speed

Exercise A: True or False?

Circle **T** for each true sentence and **F** for each false statement.

1. Playing at home gives a team an *edge* over another team. **T   F**

2. *Visualizing* means having someone watch while you practice. **T   F**

3. If a movie *rattled* the audience, it was probably a scary one. **T   F**

4. It's nice to see people *sneering* when you walk by. **T   F**

5. Turtles are often seen *barreling* through a forest. **T   F**

Exercise B: Which Word?

Choose the best word from the list to answer each question below.

1. Which word goes with *worked up*? _____

2. Which word goes with *sneaked away*? _____

3. Which word goes with *touching gently*? _____

4. Which word goes with *strutted proudly*? _____

5. Which word goes with *proved to be correct*? _____

6. Which word goes with *laughing at*? _____

UNIT 5

Selection Vocabulary Practice

The Question of Popularity (page 574)

Vocabulary

factor *n.* something that contributes to a certain result
envied *v.* felt jealous of someone
obnoxious *adj.* very disagreeable or offensive
varies *v.* changes in some way
insecurity *n.* a feeling of anxiety and lack of confidence
majority *n.* more than half; the greater part
cliques *n.* social groups
acceptance *n.* letting someone in as a member of a group
interests *n.* activities that one enjoys
exclude *v.* to leave someone or something out

Exercise A: Finding Synonyms

Cross out the word or phrase that does not belong in each group.

1. obnoxious   nasty   sweet   unpleasant

2. hobbies   pastimes   interests   careers

3. keep out   invite   exclude   prevent from joining

4. outcast   cliques   clubs   circles of friends

5. cause   outcome   factor   reason

Exercise B: Words in Context

Choose the best word from the list to complete each sentence.

1. Although Logan _____ his brother when he bought his first car, he was happy to see him do so well.

2. Sleeping in a crate reduces a new puppy's fear and _____.

3. Julianne longed for _____ at her new school.

4. The number of campers at the park _____ with the season.

5. Ms. Olson was voted into office by an overwhelming _____.

UNIT 5

Selection Vocabulary Practice

an african american   (page 588)

Vocabulary

continent *n.* one of the seven great land masses on the earth

ancestors *n.* one's relations from earlier generations

mimicked *v.* copied; imitated

desperately *adv.* in a frantic, anxious way

unison *n.* at the same time; simultaneously

croons *v.* sings softly in a low voice

anthem *n.* the official song of a country, school, or group

spiritual *n.* a religious song

barriers *n.* obstacles to achievement

Exercise A: Matching Definitions

Choose the best word from the list to match each definition.

1. song about a nation or social group _____

2. things that block one's path or progress _____

3. moving, speaking, or singing together _____

4. song about one's religious beliefs _____

Exercise B: Complete the Paragraph

Choose the best word from the list below to complete each sentence.

desperately   ancestors   croons   mimicked   continent

Rachel clicks the print icon. Nothing. With a growing sense of panic, she **(1)** _____ clicks it again and again. In her mind, the error message "Printer not responding!" appears. Seconds later the same error message appears on the computer screen. The computer had actually **(2)** _____ her thoughts. "Oh, great!" says Rachel, "I had to have the first computer on the North American **(3)** _____ that can read one's thoughts! Look, Mr. High Tech, your **(4)** _____ were washing machines and can openers! You will not mock me this way!" A stony silence. A new tactic: Rachel **(5)** _____ lovingly, "You'll help me print my report, won't you?"

Selection Vocabulary Practice

One Throw (page 596)

Vocabulary

lobby *n.* a large hall at the entrance of a building

exaggerating *v.* representing something as greater than it is; overstating

recognize *v.* to know who someone is

bawls (out) *v.* scolds loudly; yells at

egging *v.* urging; encouraging to take action

sore *adj.* angry; annoyed

expression *n.* the look on one's face

needle *v.* to cause to take action by repeated stinging comments

Exercise A: This or That?

Choose the best answer for each question.

1. Would it be *exaggerating* to say you ran a mile in ten seconds or fifteen minutes? _____

2. If you *recognize* someone, are they familiar or unfamiliar? _____

3. Would a hotel *lobby* be found on the first floor or the top floor of the building? _____

4. If a crowd is *egging* on a rider, is it encouraging her or discouraging her? _____

5. When someone has a happy *expression*, are they frowning or smiling? _____

Exercise B: Words in Context

Choose the best word from the list to complete each sentence.

1. I was happy to see my puppy _____ me and come running to me.

2. We knew Grandpa was _____, but we loved his stories.

3. Brenda was _____ when her sister forgot her birthday.

4. When I am late getting home, my mother _____ me out for not having called earlier.

5. When Kaiya continued to _____ her brother, he stopped talking to her and ignored her.

UNIT 5

Selection Vocabulary Practice

The Medicine Bag (page 608)

Vocabulary

glamorous *adj.* exciting; highly interesting
authentic *adj.* real; genuine
stately *adj.* grand; impressive; dignified
commotion *n.* a noisy, confused activity
peer *n.* to look at closely
rumpled *adj.* wrinkled and untidy
fatigue *n.* tiredness; exhaustion
embrace *v.* to hug
descendants *n.* blood relatives of an earlier generation
sacred *adj.* holy; to do with religion

Exercise A: Complete the Sentence

Write the best word from the list to complete each sentence.

1. Taking out the trash is not a _____ chore.

2. The crowd stood in awe of the _____ queen.

3. There was a big _____ when the fire alarm went off.

4. Overcome with _____, Jesse fell asleep at his desk.

5. Grace began to iron the basket of _____ clothing.

Exercise B: Context Clues

Circle **C** for each correct statement and **I** for each incorrect statement.

1. The *authentic* painting looked so real that it fooled the artist. **C I**

2. Luke stopped to *peer* at the map before heading up the trail. **C I**

3. Everyone was upset at the results, so they began to *embrace* the judges. **C I**

4. It is important to remember our *descendants* who came before us. **C I**

5. The villagers held *sacred* rituals at the base of the holy mountain. **C I**

UNIT 5

Selection Vocabulary Practice

A Year of Living Bravely (page 622)

Vocabulary

horrifying *adj.* very scary; terrifying

recovered *v.* returned to a normal state of health

self-conscious *adj.* feeling aware of one's appearance or actions

confesses *v.* tells a truth one rarely talks about

complete *adj.* whole; not missing anything

adjusted *v.* became used to something

perks *n.* special benefits; privileges

exotic *adj.* strangely beautiful and foreign

hardships *n.* things that cause pain or suffering; misfortunes

Exercise A: Matching

Write the letter of the ending that matches the beginning of each sentence.

___ **1.** After a week at home in bed, Christie…

___ **2.** The Student of the Month gets…

___ **3.** Stella found the Moroccan food…

___ **4.** Growing up, Eddie faced…

___ **5.** It took a year before Al…

A. many *hardships*.

B. quite *exotic*.

C. special *perks*.

D. finally *adjusted*.

E. *recovered* fully.

Exercise B: If . . . ?

Choose the best answer for each question.

1. If something is *horrifying*, would you enjoy it or be scared of it? _____

2. If Haroon is *self-conscious*, is he shy or confident around new people? _____

3. If Tanya *confesses* and apologizes for her mistake, will her friends stop talking to her or forgive her? _____

4. If you have read the *complete* book, did you finish reading it or will you start reading it? _____

UNIT 5

Selection Vocabulary Practice

The Fire Pond Part A (page 638)

Vocabulary

stock *v.* to supply with
blurring *v.* making less clear; causing to look fuzzy
fortune *n.* luck; riches
stranded *v.* left in a place with no way to get out
recedes *v.* moves or pulls back
salvaged *v.* saved from ruin; rescued
quarry *n.* a large open pit from which stone can be obtained
summon *v.* to call for
calculating *v.* using math or logic to figure out something
comb *v.* to go over carefully with great attention

Exercise A: True or False?

Circle **T** for each true statement and **F** for each false statement.

1. When grocery store clerks *stock* shelves, they remove products. **T   F**

2. People become *stranded* when their cars break down. **T   F**

3. They *salvaged* their clothes from the burning closet. **T   F**

4. Dial 911 to *summon* the police. **T   F**

5. A *quarry* is a field cleared for farmland. **T   F**

Exercise B: Synonyms or Antonyms?

Write **S** if the words are synonyms. Write **A** if they are antonyms.

___ **1.** blurring   clearing
___ **2.** fortune   wealth
___ **3.** recedes   advances
___ **4.** calculating   figuring out
___ **5.** comb   skim over

UNIT 5

Selection Vocabulary Practice

The Fire Pond   Part B   (page 638)

Vocabulary

darting *v.* moving quickly in different directions
seeps *v.* passes through very slowly
trudge *v.* to walk with effort
rally *v.* to call people to come together for a purpose
blaring *v.* making a loud or harsh sound
trample *v.* to tread on so heavily as to injure, crush, or destroy
stationed *v.* placed oneself in a certain spot
spooked *v.* frightened; startled
sheer *adj.* thin; nearly transparent
embers *n.* glowing pieces of wood or coal in a dying fire

Exercise: Word Search

Read the clues and guess the vocabulary words. Then search for the words in the puzzle.

1. gather for a cause _____

2. not thick _____

3. leaks through _____

4. drag oneself _____

5. crush underfoot _____

6. positioned _____

7. hot ashes _____

8. blasting _____

9. dashing _____

10. scared _____

G	R	M	J	W	A	O	D	A	V	D	O	B
I	O	S	T	A	T	I	O	N	E	D	M	L
S	M	W	H	R	D	W	H	V	D	O	A	A
E	G	J	D	T	R	A	M	P	L	E	M	R
E	J	D	M	H	O	W	H	O	J	D	A	I
P	O	A	R	V	D	H	E	G	A	S	G	N
S	M	R	G	M	L	V	J	H	H	H	D	G
A	J	T	R	R	A	L	L	Y	W	E	M	G
S	M	I	H	H	O	I	V	I	H	E	J	D
P	M	N	R	G	J	W	I	H	M	R	M	I
O	O	G	A	T	R	U	D	G	E	D	I	R
O	M	H	J	G	I	L	V	E	H	R	M	A
K	A	W	D	H	M	D	D	J	D	E	D	L
E	G	A	E	M	B	E	R	S	V	H	R	B
D	J	O	D	O	H	G	H	J	L	H	V	O

Selection Vocabulary Practice

from Savion!: My Life in Tap   (page 654)

| Vocabulary |

askew *adj.* turned or twisted to one side

hygiene *n.* cleanliness; habits that lead to good health

translates *v.* changes from one language, form, or condition to another

familiarity *n.* a sense of knowing something well

highlight *n.* the most important, interesting, or memorable part of something

humbling *v.* making someone feel less proud or important

Exercise A: Using Synonyms

Circle the words in each sentence that help you figure out the meaning of the vocabulary word.

1. The strong winds left her stole *askew*, all bunched up around her shoulders.

2. They wanted to stay healthy, so they practiced good *hygiene*.

3. Mike's *familiarity* with horses showed in his ease around them.

4. The humiliating loss to the Tadpoles swim team was *humbling* for the Sharks.

Exercise B: Context Clues

Circle **C** for each correct statement and **I** for each incorrect statement.

1. Hard work usually *translates* into failure. **C   I**

2. The *highlight* of the show was when the whole cast came out and performed a stunning musical piece together. **C   I**

3. She did not do well on the test because of her *familiarity* with the subject. **C   I**

4. It is important to wash your hands for good *hygiene*. **C   I**

UNIT 5

Selection Vocabulary Practice

A Retrieved Reformation (page 665)

Vocabulary

escorted *v.* guided; accompanied

alibi *n.* an explanation used to prove one's innocence

discharged *v.* released

compulsory *adj.* required

retribution *n.* punishment for crimes

scarce *adj.* few in number

sociable *adj.* friendly; enjoying spending time with others

duplicate *v.* to copy

venture *v.* to do something despite the risk of danger

simultaneously *adv.* at the same time

Exercise A: Matching Synonyms

Choose the word from the list that is a synonym for each clue.

1. rare _____

2. let go _____

3. outgoing _____

4. necessary _____

5. led someone _____

Exercise B: Complete the Conversation

Circle the correct word to complete the conversation.

1. MR. ADAMS: Jimmy, a little over a year ago, two of my banks were robbed almost (compulsory, simultaneously).

2. JIMMY: Sir, I have a good (alibi, sociable)!

3. MR. ADAMS: I'd like to hear it! No one could (venture, duplicate) the criminal artistry of those thieves.

4. JIMMY: Mr. Adams, a year ago I was serving a prison sentence as (retribution, escorted) for a crime I committed.

MR. ADAMS: Would you say, then, that you are a reformed man?

JIMMY: Without a doubt, sir.

5. MR. ADAMS: Then we will (discharged, venture) forth with a clean slate and speak of this no more!

UNIT 5

Selection Vocabulary Practice

A Retrieved Reformation   (page 675)

Vocabulary

rehabilitate *v.* to help to return to a normal life
disregarding *v.* not paying any attention to
leisurely *adv.* in a slow, unhurried way
boarded *v.* got on a train, airplane, or ship
fondly *adv.* with a feeling of love
eminent *adj.* of outstanding quality or rank
clemency *n.* mercy or forgiving for wrongdoing
phoenix *n.* a mythical bird that burns when it dies and is reborn from its ashes
flourishing *v.* thriving; doing extremely well
sauntered *v.* walked leisurely

Exercise A: Words in Context

Write the best word from the list to complete each sentence.

1. Luis was _____ the TV and concentrating on his homework.

2. The pilot _____ the airplane after the passengers.

3. The retired teacher _____ remembered all his students.

4. Convicted of littering in the park, the teen begged for _____.

5. The _____ psychologist gave a lecture on his famous theory.

Exercise B: Matching Synonyms

Write the letter of the synonym that matches each vocabulary word.

____ **1.** rehabilitate   **A.** laid-back
____ **2.** leisurely   **B.** doing well
____ **3.** phoenix   **C.** restore
____ **4.** flourishing   **D.** strolled
____ **5.** sauntered   **E.** bird

UNIT 5

Selection Vocabulary Practice

The Diary of Anne Frank, Act 1, Scene 3
(page 736)

Vocabulary

self-conscious *adj.* too aware of one's own appearance and actions
dignified *adj.* behaving in a calm, proper way
resent *v.* to feel angry or annoyed
absurd *adj.* not making sense; very silly
absorbed *adj.* deeply involved or occupied
vile *adj.* very bad; extremely unpleasant
mimics *v.* makes fun of by imitating or copying
aggravating *adj.* irritating; annoying
bickering *n.* a quarrel or argument, especially about minor details
meticulous *adj.* careful about small details

Exercise A: Words in Context

Choose the best word from the list to complete the sentence.

1. It's _____ to believe the moon is made of cheese.

2. Jake's dad was _____ about keeping the house clean.

3. The twins' _____ over their toys never let up.

4. Amelia felt _____ when she got her new braces.

5. The gentleman refused to wear the goofy party hat because he felt it would not be _____.

Exercise B: True or False?

Circle **T** for each true statement and **F** for each false statement.

1. A *vile* chore is one that is fun to do. **T F**

2. When a child *mimics* another child, he is being kind. **T F**

3. A student would probably *resent* having to write a 100-page report. **T F**

4. Taking a warm, relaxing bath is an *aggravating* experience. **T F**

5. If you are *absorbed* in a book, it is an interesting one. **T F**

UNIT 6

Selection Vocabulary Practice

The Diary of Anne Frank, Act 1, Scenes 4–5

Part A (page 766)

Vocabulary

accustomed *adj.* usual; customary
gradually *adv.* little by little
clinging *v.* hanging onto
improvised *v.* came up with a substitute for something
hesitates *v.* waits a moment
strain *v.* to do something with great effort
appalled *adj.* shocked and disbelieving
audible *adj.* able to be heard
weather *v.* to survive through a difficult situation or condition
dim *v.* to become less bright

Exercise A: Complete the Diary Entry

Choose the best word from the list to complete this imaginary entry from Peter Van Daan's diary.

I can't go anywhere without Anne **(1)** _____ to me like a flea on Mouschi! **(2)** _____ to being alone, I don't want to spend so much time with a girl. Yesterday, I **(3)** _____ a shade out of an old shirt for that bare light bulb in the closet. The minute I put it up, I hear a faint, barely **(4)** _____ knocking at the door. It's Anne. I **(5)** _____ open the door, bit by bit, so Mouschi will not get out. Anne pops inside and asks, "What are you doing, Peter?" I say, "Isn't it obvious? I covered the light bulb to **(6)** _____ the light." Anne is **(7)** _____. In a shocked voice, she says, "But Peter! It's so dark in here, I should think you would want to make it brighter!" Suddenly, Mouschi runs out the door and hops out the window onto the ledge. We **(8)** _____ to reach him, but he is too far away. For a moment, he **(9)** _____, then leaps to a tree and is gone. It is beginning to rain very hard. I hope that Mouschi will be able to **(10)** _____ the storm somehow. And I hope that I will be able to stand Anne for however long we are stuck here together!

UNIT 6

Selection Vocabulary Practice

The Diary of Anne Frank, Act 1, Scenes 4–5
Part B   (page 766)

Vocabulary

makeshift *adj.* used in place of the normal or proper thing

bearings *n.* knowledge of one's location; knowing where you are

endangering *v.* putting at risk

flings *v.* throws quickly and forcefully

wallow *v.* to take selfish pleasure in comfort

sustenance *n.* food, support, and other necessities of life

jubilation *n.* great joy and excitement

uncertainty *n.* the state of being unsure or not knowing

hysterically *adv.* wildly; in a way that is out of control

infinite *adj.* without any limit or number

Exercise A: Matching

Write the letter of the definition that matches each vocabulary word.

___ **1.** flings   **A.** endless

___ **2.** endangering   **B.** state of doubt

___ **3.** jubilation   **C.** putting in danger

___ **4.** infinite   **D.** tosses rapidly

___ **5.** uncertainty   **E.** extreme happiness

Exercise B: Words in Context

Choose the best word from the list to complete each sentence.

1. The _____ tent was really just a blanket strung between the couch and the dining room table.

2. Bill had to stop for a second to get his _____ so that he would not get lost in the woods.

3. Cindy's mean step-sisters liked to _____ in their wealth while she had only one change of clothing.

4. Bella decided that they had to stop shopping because they needed _____.

5. Mick's sister was crying _____ because we couldn't find her cat.

UNIT 6

Selection Vocabulary Practice

The Diary of Anne Frank, Act 2, Scenes 1–2
(page 798)

Vocabulary

standstill *n.* when all action stops and further action is prevented

disgruntled *adj.* not pleased; in a bad mood

foreboding *n.* a feeling that something bad has happened or will happen

reassure *v.* to say comforting things to make someone feel better

apprehension *n.* fear of what may happen

blackmail *n.* forcing someone to pay money so that secret or private information will not be revealed

intimate *adj.* very close and personal; private

intuition *n.* the ability to know things without having to reason them out

poise *n.* a calm, relaxed, and self-controlled manner

Exercise A: Words in Context

Read the paragraph. Circle the best word to complete each sentence below.

Jennifer felt a sense of *foreboding* as she knocked on Sheri's door. They had never been *intimate* friends. Jennifer's *intuition* told her something was wrong. Jennifer saw her diary in Sheri's hand. With *poise*, Jennifer said, "So, you're planning some kind of *blackmail*?" "Yup!" said Sheri.

1. Jennifer felt (excited, worried) about visiting Sheri.

2. Jennifer and Sheri (were, were not) best friends.

3. Jennifer (sensed, figured out) that something was wrong.

4. Jennifer spoke (calmly, nervously) to Sheri.

5. Sheri planned to (help, take advantage of) Jennifer.

Exercise B: This or That?

Choose the best answer for each question.

1. If a car comes to a *standstill*, has it turned or stopped? _____

2. If a mother feels *apprehension*, is she worried or proud? _____

3. If a teacher is *disgruntled,* is he cheerful or grouchy? _____

4. If a friend tries to *reassure* you, does she want to make you feel better or worse? _____

UNIT 6

Selection Vocabulary Practice

The Diary of Anne Frank, Act 2, Scenes 3–5

Part A   (page 826)

Vocabulary

frenzy *n.* a brief loss of reason and control
obligation *n.* something one must do, especially in return for getting something
bewildered *adj.* completely confused
remorse *n.* a feeling of being sorry for having done something
succession *n.* the act of one thing following after another
post *n.* a place one is assigned to guard
whimper *v.* to cry weakly from pain or fear
insistent *adj.* stubbornly demanding something
abruptly *adv.* suddenly
bitterness *n.* a sense of angry sadness

Exercise: Crossword Puzzle

Use the clues to solve the puzzle.

ACROSS
1. appointed spot
4. sob quietly
5. a duty to repay
8. unhappy anger
10. regret for one's actions

DOWN
2. a series of things
3. puzzled
6. firm and forceful
7. all of a sudden
9. wild behavior

UNIT 6

Selection Vocabulary Practice

The Diary of Anne Frank, Act 2, Scenes 3–5
Part B   (page 826)

Vocabulary

stealthily *adv.* in a secret or sneaky manner
rigid *adj.* stiff
indignation *n.* anger about something thought to be unjust or unfair
choicest *adj.* best; most desirable
invasion *n.* the act of entering enemy territory
pandemonium *n.* wild disorder and uproar
liberated *adj.* released; freed
feeble *adj.* very weak
downcast *adj.* sad; depressed
tension *n.* a state of suspense and worry

Exercise A: True or False?

Circle **T** for each true statement and **F** for each false statement.

1. A shirt ironed with too much starch is *rigid*. **T   F**

2. The *choicest* diamonds are the most expensive. **T   F**

3. When a butterfly is *liberated*, it is kept in a jar. **T   F**

4. Someone who is very sick may feel *feeble*. **T   F**

5. A team will feel *downcast* after they win a big game. **T   F**

Exercise B: Context Clues

Circle the words in the sentence that help you figure out the meaning of each vocabulary word.

1. The *tension* made Beth fidget, chewing her fingernails.

2. The dog crept up to the picnic table and *stealthily* swiped a steak.

3. The angry audience was full of *indignation* when the movie broke.

4. The *invasion* started when the troops stormed the enemy's fort.

5. The *pandemonium* peaked when the crowd climbed the goalposts.

Selection Vocabulary Practice

Bouncing Back *and* Another Mountain   (page 850)

Vocabulary

unfulfilling *adj.* not satisfying
resilient *adj.* able to recover from or adjust easily to misfortune or change
strategies *n.* plans for working through a problem or activity
temporary *adj.* not permanent; not lasting forever
tackling *v.* taking on a difficult activity
phase *n.* a step in the development of a person or thing
mentors *n.* guides; coaches; role models
destitute *adj.* completely without money or possessions
avalanche *n.* a sudden, overwhelming amount
plateau *n.* a large, flat area of high land

Exercise A: Context Clues

Circle the words in the sentence that help you figure out the meaning of each vocabulary word.

1. When Al's first plan did not work, he came up with new *strategies*.

2. The *temporary* tattoo lasted only a brief time before it wore off.

3. With the first *phase* of the project done, Jena went to the next stage.

4. The tsunami left people *destitute* in the already poor country.

5. The *plateau* was an ideal spot for a lookout tower.

Exercise B: Sentence Completion

Complete each sentence.

1. The ending of a movie might be *unfulfilling* if _____.

2. After getting a bad grade, a *resilient* student will _____.

3. When *tackling* a hard chore, it is a good idea to _____.

4. *Mentors* can help young people by _____.

5. You might have to do an *avalanche* of homework if you _____.

UNIT 6

Selection Vocabulary Practice

Standing Tall   (page 862)

Vocabulary

sturdier *adj.* stronger
tribute *n.* an action or gift that shows respect, admiration, or thanks
collapse *v.* to fall apart, cave in, or break down
shatter *v.* to break into small pieces
stable *adj.* firm and steady; long-lasting
withstand *v.* to resist the effect of; stand up against
enable *v.* to give strength, power, or ability; to make able
zone *n.* a separate area with a special use

Exercise A: Mystery Word

Choose the best word from the list to complete each sentence.
Unscramble the circled letters to discover the mystery word.

1. The building was made to __ __ __ __ __ __(__)__ the force of an earthquake.

2. The statue was a __ __ __ __ __(__) to World War II veterans.

3. After being laid off, Jim looked for a more __ __ __(__)__ __ job.

4. A rock caused the windshield to __ __(__)__ __ __ .

5. The old bridge looked like it might __ __(__)__ __ __ __(__) soon.

Mystery Word __ __ __ __ __ __

Exercise B: Context Clues

Circle **C** for each correct statement and **I** for each incorrect statement.

1. Horses are *sturdier* than people and can carry heavier loads. **C   I**

2. The city created a special *zone* to preserve historic buildings. **C   I**

3. Scholarships *enable* many students to go to college. **C   I**

4. The destroyed building was able to *withstand* the tornado. **C   I**

5. The Johnsons' *stable* marriage was rocky and stressful. **C   I**

6. The metal cups were likely to *shatter* if dropped. **C   I**

UNIT 6

Selection Vocabulary Practice

from Sky   **(page 882)**

Vocabulary

grave *adj.* very serious; likely to produce harm or danger
anticipation *n.* the act of looking forward to; expectation
falsified *adj.* fake items made to seem genuine
transporting *v.* taking from one place to another
precautions *n.* actions taken to prevent difficulty before it happens
observant *adj.* quick to notice or observe; alert; watchful
amiss *adj.* wrong; not as it should be
dreaded *v.* feared greatly
uneventful *adj.* with nothing out of the ordinary happening

Exercise A: Word Groups

Cross out the word or phrase that does not belong in each group.

1. dangerous   grave   silly   serious
2. made up   faked   falsified   real
3. moving   carrying   staying   transporting
4. boring   unexciting   uneventful   action-packed
5. dreaded   terrified of   welcomed   afraid of

Exercise B: Words in Context

Circle the best word to complete each sentence.

1. WOMAN: Hanneke, is something (amiss, uneventful)? You look troubled today.
2. HANNEKE: You are very (uneventful, observant)! I am a little shaken up after my last assignment.
3. WOMAN: I pray that nothing (falsified, grave) happened.
4. HANNEKE: I am afraid that in spite of all our (precautions, transporting), we had our IDs checked by German soldiers.
5. WOMAN: Are you resigning from the Resistance?
6. HANNEKE: On the contrary! I look forward with great (anticipation, uneventful) to my next assignment.
7. WOMAN: Excellent!

UNIT 6

Selection Vocabulary Practice

Welcome (page 893)

Vocabulary

dismal *adj.* gloomy or depressing

hazy *adj.* not clear in thought or meaning

souvenir *n.* something kept to remind one of a place or time

saddle *v.* burden; load down

ultimatum *n.* a final demand that, if unmet, carries harsh penalties

famished *adj.* extremely hungry

pivoted *v.* turned around sharply

coaxed *v.* urged gently

Exercise A: Words in Context

Choose the best word from the list to complete each sentence.

1. I was a little _____ about the details, so I asked Ms. Henks to explain.

2. Lee picked up a small _____ from every place he visited.

3. Cecila's mother issued her an _____: either she cleaned her room or everything would get thrown out.

4. It was a _____ setting for a picnic until the sun came out.

5. Christy _____ to see who had called her name behind her.

Exercise B: Synonyms or Antonyms?

Write **S** if the words are synonyms. Write **A** if they are antonyms.

___ **1.** dismal, sad

___ **2.** hazy, clear

___ **3.** saddle, relieve

___ **4.** famished, starving

___ **5.** coaxed, persuaded

Exercise C: Responding to the Selection

Imagine that you are Tina in "Welcome." You have decided to keep the bag that Aunt Dessie gave you. On a separate sheet of paper, write a letter to Aunt Dessie to thank her for the present. Use at least four of the vocabulary words.

Copyright © by The McGraw-Hill Companies, Inc.

UNIT 6

Selection Vocabulary Practice

Saving Water: Why Save Something That Covers Two-thirds of the Earth? (page 934)

Vocabulary

fixed *adj.* a set amount

misuse *v.* to use in the wrong way or for the wrong purpose

vast *adj.* very great in number or size

municipal *adj.* having to do with a city or town or its government

distribution *n.* a division into shares or portions

contamination *n.* pollution

usage *n.* the act of using

approximately *adv.* very much like; close to

rushing *v.* moving quickly

swig *n.* a big swallow of something liquid

Exercise A: Words in Context

Choose the best word from the list to complete each sentence.

1. The Rockies are a _____ mountain range.

2. People on a _____ income need to spend money carefully.

3. After the flood, the relief agency handled the _____ of food.

4. _____ half of the students took part in the book fair.

5. The canoe was swept down the _____ river.

Exercise B: Matching

Write the letter of the vocabulary word that is the synonym of each word.

____ **1.** impurity   **A.** misuse

____ **2.** practice   **B.** municipal

____ **3.** local   **C.** contamination

____ **4.** drink   **D.** usage

____ **5.** abuse   **E.** swig

Exercise C: Responding to the Selection

Imagine that you have been asked to write a public service announcement (PSA) about saving water. On a separate sheet of paper, write your PSA. Use at least four of the vocabulary words.

Leveled Vocabulary Development, ELL

UNIT 7

Selection Vocabulary Practice

from The Measure of Our Success   (page 944)

Vocabulary

upbringing *n.* the way one is raised as a child
respond *v.* to react or answer
watchful *adj.* alert; careful
entitled *v.* deserved a right to something
persistence *n.* the act of refusing to give up
tolerate *v.* to let something happen or exist without trying to stop it
corruption *n.* extreme immorality; wickedness
racial *adj.* having to do with race or an ethnic or cultural group
illiterate *adj.* unable to read or write; uneducated

Exercise A: This or That?

Choose the best answer for each question.

1. If a mountain climber has *persistence,* will he give up or keep going?

2. Would a *watchful* neighbor notice or not notice a house being robbed?

3. If you *tolerate* a dog licking your face, do you stop it or let it go on?

4. Would an *illiterate* person study or not study a magazine article?

5. If Jason were *entitled* to win the medal, would his chances of winning be high or low?

Exercise B: Mystery Word

Write the vocabulary word for each clue. Unscramble the circled letters to discover the mystery word.

1. qualified for Ⓞ_ _ _ _ _ _ Ⓞ

2. determination _ _ _Ⓞ_ _ _ _Ⓞ_

3. dishonesty _ _ _ _ _ _ _Ⓞ_

4. background Ⓞ_ _ _ _ _ _ _ _ _

5. ethnic Ⓞ_ _ _ _ _

Mystery Word _ _ _ _ _ _ _ _

UNIT 7

Selection Vocabulary Practice

All Together Now (page 960)

Vocabulary

harmonious *adj.* getting along well together; friendly
ensured *v.* made certain
regained *v.* got back
diverse *adj.* different; not alike
indispensable *adj.* absolutely necessary
nurture *v.* to take care of; to help grow or develop
incurable *adj.* not likely to be changed or corrected
optimist *n.* a person who has a positive or cheerful outlook
labor *n.* work; task
fellow *adj.* in the same way or situation

Exercise A: Complete the Sentence

Circle the letter of the best word to complete each sentence.

1. The coach _____ that each kid had a chance to play.
   A. regained   **B.** labor   **C.** ensured

2. As soon as Quentin _____ his strength, he went back to work.
   A. diverse   **B.** nurture   **C.** regained

3. Jen is an _____; she believes everything will turn out fine.
   A. harmonious   **B.** optimist   **C.** incurable

4. My _____ Americans, the future of our country is up to us.
   A. incurable   **B.** ensured   **C.** fellow

5. Many hours of _____ went into building the tree house.
   A. labor   **B.** nurture   **C.** indispensable

Exercise B: Context Clues

Circle **C** for each correct statement and **I** for each incorrect statement.

1. The Smiths had a *harmonious* marriage and rarely argued. **C   I**

2. Stephen recovered from the *incurable* disease in a week. **C   I**

3. A first-aid kit is an *indispensable* item on a camping trip. **C   I**

4. The school's *diverse* population is a mixture of many cultures. **C   I**

UNIT 7

Selection Vocabulary Practice

from **Through My Eyes**   (page 968)

Vocabulary

assemble *v.* to gather together in a group
dismounted *v.* got off of or down from something
clustered *v.* formed small groups
taunts *n.* hurtful or mocking remarks
gripped *v.* held onto tightly
barricades *n.* barriers put up to separate or for defense
integrated *v.* ended the separation of racial and ethnic groups
verses *n.* sections of a poem or song
uneasy *adj.* nervous; uncomfortable
enforce *v.* to make people obey

Exercise A: Matching

Write the letter of the ending that matches the beginning of each sentence.

___ **1.** At his first job interview, Rick	**A.** *enforce* the rules.
___ **2.** As she began to sing, Ellen suddenly	**B.** *dismounted* sadly.
___ **3.** After the 1960s, most schools	**C.** forgot the first *verses*.
___ **4.** After losing the horse race, the jockey	**D.** *integrated* all students.
___ **5.** The easygoing teacher did not try to	**E.** felt *uneasy*.

Exercise B: Complete the Sentence

Choose the best word from the list to complete each sentence.

1. Students _____ at school when there is a pep rally.

2. _____ are used at car races to prevent accidents.

3. The kids were scared and _____ around their parents.

4. Sue _____ the dashboard and told Jim to slow down.

5. The marchers ignored the _____ of the angry crowd.

Exercise C: Responding to the Selection

In the story, some boys changed the words to a song to protest integration. On a separate sheet of paper, change the words to a song to support integration. Use four vocabulary words.

UNIT 7

Selection Vocabulary Practice

The Trouble with Television   Part A   (page 980)

Vocabulary

rewarding *adj.* giving great satisfaction
gratification *n.* pleasure or satisfaction
perpetual *adj.* continuing forever
allotted *adj.* assigned
passively *adv.* not actively
enhances *v.* improves or makes better
strain *v.* to stretch to the limit; to overwork
virtually *adv.* nearly; almost
skeptically *adv.* with doubt

Exercise A: Fill in the Boxes

Choose the best word from the list to fill in the boxes.

1. increases the beauty of

2. questioningly

3. enjoyment

4. tire a muscle

Exercise B: Synonyms or Antonyms?

Write **S** if the words are synonyms. Write **A** if they are antonyms.

___ 1. perpetual, never-ending

___ 2. allotted, withheld

___ 3. passively, energetically

___ 4. virtually, practically

___ 5. rewarding, pleasing

Exercise C: Responding to the Selection

Imagine that you are participating in a debate on whether television has a positive or negative influence on kids. On a separate sheet of paper, list five major points you will make when it is your turn to speak. Use at least four of the vocabulary words.

UNIT 7

Selection Vocabulary Practice

The Trouble with Television Part B (page 980)

Vocabulary

constructive *adj.* having the ability to help develop or improve
inefficient *adj.* wasteful of time, energy, or material
simplistic *adj.* too simple or basic
dominating *adj.* main; central; having the most influence
resolutions *n.* answers or solutions
earnest *adj.* serious and sincere

Exercise A: MacNeil's Bumper Sticker

Find the vocabulary word in the scrambled letters. Use the leftover letters to write the bumper sticker that Robert MacNeil might have on his car.

1. helpful; productive CSONESTRULCTIVE _____

2. disorganized; unproductive LINEFYFICOIENT _____

3. too easy SUIMRPLITSTIC _____

4. overriding; major EDOLMIENATING _____

5. answers REVSIOLUTISONS _____

6. intense and heartfelt IEARONESNT _____

___ ___ ___ ___ ___ ___ ___ ___ ___ ___ ___ ___ ___ ___ ___ ___ ___ !!!

Exercise B: Responding to the Selection

On a separate sheet of paper, write your own bumper sticker either for or against television. Use at least one of the vocabulary words.

Selection Vocabulary Practice

Teen Curfews (page 988)

Vocabulary

targeted *v.* focused on
aced *v.* earned a high grade; did very well
convictions *n.* strong beliefs or values
controversial *adj.* causing disagreement
violating *v.* breaking or disregarding a law
overturn *v.* to reverse a legal judgment
scapegoated *v.* blamed for something that someone else has done
curbing *v.* holding back; controlling
delinquent *adj.* breaking the law or not following the rules
predators *n.* people who steal from or do harm to others

Exercise A: Words in Context

Choose the best word from the list to complete each sentence.

1. Margot was thrilled when she _____ her science test.

2. The subject of school uniforms can be a _____ issue.

3. There is a big fine for _____ the speed limit.

4. Not telling the truth went against Ryan's _____ about honesty.

5. _____ littering at the beach was the town council's main concern.

Exercise B: Context Clues

Circle **C** for each correct statement and **I** for each incorrect statement.

1. The new toy commercial *targeted* kids under five years old. **C I**

2. The environmental group wanted to *overturn* the law that protected the near-extinct lizard. **C I**

3. Rafael proved his innocence after the others *scapegoated* him. **C I**

4. The *delinquent* teen received a medal for good citizenship. **C I**

5. Human *predators* often prey on senior citizens. **C I**

UNIT 7

Selection Vocabulary Practice

Rally for Better Food (page 1002)

Vocabulary

rally *n.* a large, organized meeting for a special purpose
boycott *v.* to refuse to use as a sign of protest
bogus *adj.* bad; not real or genuine
grub *n.* food
attend *v.* to go to; to be present at
nutritious *adj.* containing or giving nourishment

Exercise A: Matching

Write the letter of the vocabulary word that means the same as
each word or phrase.

___ **1.** healthy to eat   **A.** boycott
___ **2.** to be there   **B.** bogus
___ **3.** stop using   **C.** grub
___ **4.** edibles; "chow"   **D.** attend
___ **5.** fake; phony   **E.** nutritious

Exercise B: Context Clues

Circle the words in the sentence that help you figure out the
meaning of each vocabulary word.

1. Hundreds of people came to the *rally* to protest the decision to
tear down the historic building.

2. People refused to ride the bus during the citywide *boycott*.

3. The *bogus* scientist fooled everyone with his fake college diploma.

4. "Let's get some *grub*," David said to his friends as they walked
into the restaurant.

5. The *nutritious* shake provided ten essential vitamins and
minerals.

Exercise C: Responding to the Selection

On a separate sheet of paper, design your own poster for a rally to
protest something you would like to see changed at your school.
Use at least three of the vocabulary words in your poster.

UNIT 7

Selection Vocabulary Practice

Stop the Sun (page 1008)

Vocabulary

awkward *adj.* clumsy

syndrome *n.* a group of symptoms that, together, point to a certain disease

dry *adj.* dull or boring; not interesting

involvement *n.* the act of being a part of something

browsed *v.* looked through in a casual way

squirming *v.* twisting and turning one's body like a snake

blurted *v.* said all of a sudden without thinking

foundered *v.* broke down; collapsed

ruin *n.* a state of being completely destroyed

inert *adj.* without power to move or act; lifeless

Exercise A: Words in Context

Choose the best word from the list to complete each sentence.

1. The puppy was so tired he became _____ and could not move.

2. The child was _____ so much, her mother had to hold her tighter.

3. The factory building was a _____ after the big fire.

4. Tommy _____ out in words whatever he was thinking.

5. The doctor tried to find a _____ that matched her patient's symptoms.

6. The audience found the concert _____ and unexciting.

7. The students _____ the Internet looking for information.

Exercise B: If . . . ?

Choose the best answer for each question.

1. If the dancers are *awkward*, are they graceful or graceless? _____

2. If Jacob has no *involvement* in a crime, is he guilty or innocent? _____

3. If a television show is *dry*, is it funny or unexciting? _____

4. If Yumi *foundered*, was she upset or joyful? _____

5. If Cara *browsed*, did she shop with or without a purpose? _____

Leveled Vocabulary Development, ELL

UNIT 7

Selection Vocabulary Practice

Teens Tackle Pollution in Their Communities
(page 1021)

Vocabulary

environmentalists *n.* people concerned about the earth's environment
perseverance *n.* the act of continuing in spite of problems
toxic *adj.* poisonous
rural *adj.* relating to the countryside
emit *v.* to give off
empowered *adj.* made to feel powerful
buoyed *adj.* supported or uplifted
testified *v.* declared or provided evidence of truth in a court of law
specifications *n.* exact instructions on how something is to be done
ultimate *adj.* final; eventual

Exercise A: True or False?

Circle **T** for each true statement and **F** for each false statement.

1. A set of *specifications* gives you a rough idea of how to do a job. **T   F**

2. A *rural* setting may consist of farmlands and forests. **T   F**

3. *Toxic* chemicals should be kept away from children. **T   F**

4. It is hard to get anything done if you have *perseverance*. **T   F**

5. *Environmentalists* believe in recycling reusable items. **T   F**

Exercise B: Complete the Sentence

Choose the best word from the list to complete each sentence.

1. In court, the witness _____ that Maryann was home on the night of the accident.

2. When frightened, skunks _____ a bad odor.

3. Teens feel more _____ when they are able to make some decisions on their own.

4. When a team is behind, the players can be _____ up by the cheering of their fans.

5. The _____ reason students should stay in school is to gain skills and knowledge that will help them in the future.

UNIT 7

Selection Vocabulary Practice

A Change in Climate (page 1027)

Vocabulary

trends *n.* general patterns
droughts *n.* long periods without rain
drastic *adj.* severe; radical
impact *n.* a strong effect
accumulate *v.* to gather or build up
skeptical *adj.* doubtful
habitats *n.* particular areas where certain plants and animals are found
specialized *adj.* designed or fitted for one particular thing or purpose
vulnerable *adj.* exposed to danger
alarming *adj.* raising great concern

Exercise A: Words in Context

Circle the letter of the best word to complete each sentence.

1. The recent _____ caused some creeks to dry up completely.
   A. impact   **B.** habitats   **C.** droughts

2. Valerie was _____ that the old car would even start.
   A. drastic   **B.** skeptical   **C.** specialized

3. The crumbling walls of the fort made it _____ to attack.
   A. vulnerable   **B.** alarming   **C.** accumulate

4. Koalas have a very _____ diet; they only eat eucalyptus leaves.
   A. skeptical   **B.** specialized   **C.** drastic

5. Humans can live in a variety of different _____.
   A. droughts   **B.** trends   **C.** habitats

Exercise B: Word Scramble

Using the clues, unscramble and write each vocabulary word.

1. movements; directions ERNTSD _____

2. collect; store AMLCUCUTAE _____

3. influence; meaning PICMAT _____

4. extreme; harsh ADCRSTI _____

5. frightening; shocking LAMRNAGI _____

UNIT 7

Selection Vocabulary Practice

Volar   (Page 1068)

Vocabulary

avid *adj.* very eager or enthusiastic

recurring *adj.* happening or coming back again; repeating

fantasy *n.* an imagined scene or image; something that exists only in one's mind

adolescence *n.* the period between childhood and adulthood

abruptly *adv.* suddenly; unexpectedly

refuse *n.* trash; rubbish

inspired *v.* gave someone an idea or motivation to do something

Exercise A: Synonyms

Circle the word that is a synonym of the vocabulary word.

1. An *avid* outdoorsman, Josh was an enthusiastic skier and hiker.

2. Joe thinks his *fantasy* of building a spaceship is an achievable dream.

3. Sara's *recurring* nightmare of a giant squid was a frequent occurrence.

4. Almost at the top floor, the elevator suddenly stopped *abruptly*.

5. The park was strewn with *refuse*; even the trees were covered with trash.

Exercise B: Context Clues

Circle **C** for each correct statement and **I** for each incorrect statement.

1. We left the party *abruptly* when we heard it was later than our curfew. **C I**

2. Well into her *adolescence*, Grandma Smith was still able to drive. **C I**

3. The beautiful sunset *inspired* Mikhail to paint outdoors that day. **C I**

4. Jeri, an *avid* bicyclist, let her bike gather dust in the garage. **C I**

5. The detectives noticed a *recurring* pattern of robberies happening in one neighborhood. **C I**

Selection Vocabulary Practice

from The Century for Young People (page 1076)

Vocabulary

operated *v.* ran an organization or business

literally *adv.* actually; exactly

accumulated *v.* gathered or piled up, little by little

passage *n.* a trip; a going over from one place to another

overwhelmed *v.* overpowered in thought or feeling; completely covered or flooded

means *n.* methods useful for achieving a particular purpose or goal; resources

audience *n.* a formal meeting or interview

admitted *v.* accepted into a school, program, or organization

Exercise A: Multiple Choice

Circle the letter of the best word to complete each sentence.

1. The _____ from Asia to America took a long time.
   A. passage   **B.** means   **C.** audience

2. Enough rain water _____ to flood the streets of the town.
   A. overwhelmed   **B.** operated   **C.** accumulated

3. Bicycling is a fun and healthy _____ of transportation.
   A. audience   **B.** means   **C.** operated

4. The park committee requested an _____ with the mayor.
   A. operated   **B.** admitted   **C.** audience

5. Glenna was happy to find out she had been _____ to Yale.
   A. admitted   **B.** literally   **C.** overwhelmed

Exercise B: Complete the Sentence

Choose the best word from the list to complete each sentence.

1. Babysitting is a good example of a business _____ by a teen.

2. The No Talking sign meant _____ be silent.

3. A student might feel _____ if he or she has a lot of classes.

4. By the time Nancy left work, a lot of snow had _____ on the ground.

5. A ballerina _____ into a famous dance company would feel very happy.

Leveled Vocabulary Development, ELL

UNIT 8

Selection Vocabulary Practice

Lottery Winners Who Lost Their Millions
(page 1090)

Vocabulary

reality *n.* real life
regret *v.* to feel sorry for having done something
siblings *n.* brothers and sisters
pestered *v.* nagged; bothered
irresponsible *adj.* not careful; not thinking before acting
eventually *adv.* happening at last; in the end
lengthy *adj.* lasting a long time
inevitable *adj.* sure to happen; unavoidable
windfall *n.* receiving money or a good thing unexpectedly
consequences *n.* results or effects of an action

Exercise A: Word Groups

Cross out the word that does not belong in each group.

1. sorry   joy   regret   sadness
2. bonus   gain   windfall   loss
3. firstly   lastly   eventually   finally
4. inevitable   certain   decided   unsure
5. long-winded   lengthy   brief   drawn-out

Exercise B: Synonyms or Antonyms?

Write **S** if the words are synonyms. Write **A** if they are antonyms.
___ 1. reality, dream-world
___ 2. pestered, annoyed
___ 3. consequences, results
___ 4. irresponsible, dependable
___ 5. siblings, strangers

Selection Vocabulary Practice

The Gettysburg Address (page 1098)

Vocabulary

conceived *v.* formed; imagined
proposition *n.* a plan or proposal
endure *v.* to carry on; survive; last
detract *v.* to take away from; reduce the value of
advanced *v.* developed; made progress
task *n.* a job that needs to be done
devotion *n.* a deep love, commitment, and loyalty
resolve *v.* to decide firmly
vain *adj.* without purpose or meaning
perish *v.* to become ruined or destroyed; die

Exercise A: Words in Context

Choose the best word from the list to complete each sentence.

1. Many creative ideas can be _____ by brainstorming.

2. Bad service can _____ from a restaurant dining experience.

3. The workers were praised for the speed with which they _____ their project.

4. Mrs. Ruiz's hard work was evidence of her _____ to teaching.

5. Jackson tried in _____ to convince Amanda not to move to Hollywood to become an actress.

Exercise B: Match the Clue

Choose the best word from the list to match each clue.

1. what a person puts forth for consideration _____

2. what marathon runners need to do to run long distances _____

3. what you put off doing because you might not enjoy it _____

4. what most people do every New Year's Day _____

5. what may happen to an endangered species of animals if people are not concerned _____

UNIT 8

Selection Vocabulary Practice

I Chose Schooling (page 1106)

Vocabulary

prevailed *v.* conquered; won; overcame
interacting *v.* working with; being involved with
monumental *adj.* great and meaningful
defines *v.* creates who or what someone is; molds; influences
attaining *v.* achieving, accomplishing, or succeeding
rigorously *adv.* with great energy and thoroughness
motivation *n.* a need or desire that makes one do something
crucial *adj.* extremely important
studious *adj.* serious about studying
agitated *adj.* disturbed; upset

Exercise A: Matching

Write the letter of the synonym that matches each vocabulary word.

____ 1. prevailed   **A.** accomplishing
____ 2. interacting   **B.** dealing with
____ 3. attaining   **C.** shapes
____ 4. rigorously   **D.** succeeded
____ 5. defines   **E.** intensely

Exercise B: Context Clues

Circle the words in the sentence that help you figure out the meaning of each vocabulary word.

1. Renee's *motivation* arises from the desire to give her best to everything she does.

2. The best experience of Ruthie's life was the *monumental* moment when she stood on the podium to receive a gold medal for swimming.

3. It was *crucial* for John to go to college; his parents had always stressed the importance of a college education.

4. The *studious* girl spent every night at the library doing her homework.

5. Before the earthquake, some of the animals at the zoo became *agitated*, pacing restlessly back and forth.

Selection Vocabulary Practice

The Electric Summer (page 1114)

Vocabulary

novelty *n.* anything new, strange, or unusual

bristled *v.* showed anger or annoyance

grandeur *n.* the state of being large and impressive; greatness

daredevil *n.* a person who takes great risks

hovering *v.* remaining in or near one place; suspended in air

replica *n.* a faithful copy

rapture *n.* a feeling of great joy

seasoned *v.* made fit by experience

secured *v.* held down; attached tightly

Exercise A: Words in Context

Read the paragraph and circle the best word to complete each sentence.

The *novelty* of the snow brought all the kids out of their homes, screaming with *rapture*. The older kids gathered at the top of *Daredevil* Hill with their snowboards. They always went down the east side of the hill. Nobody, even the most *seasoned* snowboarders, went down the west side. When Frankie showed up, the teasing began: "Come on, Frankie! Go down the west side!" Frankie *bristled* and said, "You first!"

1. The scene takes place during the (first, last) snow storm.

2. The kids are (delighted, depressed) about the snow.

3. The hill got its name because it is (safe, dangerous).

4. The experienced kids (always, never) went down the west side.

5. Frankie felt (sad, annoyed) by the other kids.

Exercise B: If . . . ?

Choose the correct answer for each question.

1. If a park has *grandeur*, is it more likely in the mountains or in a city? _____

2. If a kite is *hovering*, is it staying in one place or climbing into the air? _____

3. If a painting is a *replica*, is it more or less expensive than the original? _____

4. If a captain *secured* her ship to the dock, will it stay or float away? _____

Selection Vocabulary Practice

from Dandelion Wine   Part A   (page 1142)

Vocabulary

suspended *v.* attached from above to allow free movement
capsize *v.* to overturn or upset (especially a boat)
proprietor *n.* a person or firm that owns a property or business
rave *v.* to speak about very favorably or with great enthusiasm
alien *adj.* strange; odd; peculiar
flex *v.* to bend at a joint; tense and loosen a muscle repeatedly
yielding *adj.* giving way to force or pressure
revelation *n.* a sudden, new idea or insight
bounded *v.* walked or jumped with great energy

Exercise A: True or False?

Circle **T** for each true statement and **F** for each false statement.

1. When a leaf is *suspended*, it has fallen to the ground. **T F**

2. A parent *yielding* to a child would buy the child a toy. **T F**

3. If a squirrel *bounded* across a street, it was walking very slowly. **T F**

4. It might be a *revelation* to a teenager that adults sometimes know what they are talking about. **T F**

Exercise B: Complete the Sentence

Choose the best word from the list to complete each sentence.

1. The instructor told Karl not to stand in the canoe; it could _____.

2. You would ask to talk to the _____ of a store if you wanted to make a suggestion.

3. The doctor asked Jeremy to _____ his muscles during the physical examination.

4. Susan was happy to hear her son _____ about his new teacher.

5. It would seem _____ for a grandparent to dance hip-hop.

Selection Vocabulary Practice

from Dandelion Wine   Part B   (page 1142)

Vocabulary

seized *v.* grabbed hold of
irritable *adj.* annoyed; cranky; grouchy
airy *adj.* light; like the air
detached *adj.* separated from
limber *adj.* able to bend easily
hushed *v.* became quiet
emporium *n.* a large store
vanished *v.* disappeared

Exercise: Word Search

Read the clues and guess the vocabulary words. Then, search for the words in the puzzle.

1. cut off from _____
2. flexible _____
3. went away _____
4. took forcefully _____

5. a superstore _____
6. silenced _____
7. grumpy _____
8. weightless _____

V	O	R	B	L	I	M	B	E	R	E	V	O
R	M	V	E	Q	M	T	Z	O	W	T	O	V
N	G	T	R	M	Z	E	M	D	Z	V	N	A
E	D	E	T	A	C	H	E	D	B	M	L	N
V	M	T	M	L	M	Q	N	W	O	V	Q	I
Q	E	V	N	Z	W	G	W	Z	L	T	M	S
M	G	I	R	R	I	T	A	B	L	E	G	H
H	L	Q	E	M	N	G	N	D	B	N	L	E
U	G	V	O	G	V	G	R	V	R	T	V	D
S	O	L	N	Q	M	Z	W	L	D	L	G	T
H	T	Z	L	E	Z	M	Z	R	A	I	R	Y
E	O	M	I	T	Q	G	L	V	L	W	D	G
D	L	V	R	E	M	P	O	R	I	U	M	D
L	Q	T	S	E	I	Z	E	D	T	L	G	M
V	O	R	E	M	Z	Q	L	M	N	Z	R	E

UNIT 8

Selection Vocabulary Practice

Coming to America (page 1155)

Vocabulary

newcomers *n.* people newly arrived to an area

toiled *v.* worked hard

version *n.* one's own story about what happened

era *n.* a period of time

rethinking *v.* thinking about again, in order to make changes

track *v.* to stay aware of something or someone's location or movements

consider *v.* to think or believe

emigrate *v.* to leave one country to go live in another

discriminates *v.* treats unfairly

Exercise A: Mystery Word

Choose the best word from the list to complete each sentence.
Unscramble the circled letters to discover the mystery word.

1. Jack __( )_ _( )__ for hours mowing the enormous lawn.

2. Megan told her __ __ _( )_ __ of what happened.

3. Emma is ( )_ _ _ _ _ _ _ _ _ the shag carpet in her room.

4. Radio collars are used to __ __ _( )_ bear activity in the wild.

5. An unfair law ( )_ _ _ _ _ _ _( )_ _ _ against people.

Mystery word: __ __ __ __ __ __ __ __

Exercise B: Words in Context

Read the paragraph and circle the best word or phrase to complete
each sentence.

One of the *newcomers* said, "Yes, we chose to *emigrate* from our country,
but we do not *consider* our country to be completely bad. It is just in a
dangerous *era* in which the law *discriminates* against the poor."

1. The speaker had (been born, just arrived) in the United States.

2. The speaker (is going to, has moved from) his native country.

3. The speaker's country is going through a difficult (decision, time).

4. In his country, the law (helps, hurts) the poor.

Selection Vocabulary Practice

Coming to America   (page 1162)

Vocabulary

sponsor *v.* to take responsibility for another person
trivial *adj.* of very little value or importance
asylum *n.* a permission to live, work, and become a citizen of a country
incongruous *adj.* not in agreement; out of place
ordeal *n.* a difficult experience
immersed *v.* completely occupied mentally
excel *v.* to do or be better than others
struggle *n.* great effort spent trying to achieve something

Exercise A: This or That?

Choose the best answer for each question.

1. If you wanted to *sponsor* Norbu, would you help her or stand in her way? _____

2. If a problem were *trivial*, would it be a big deal or not a big deal? _____

3. Would an *incongruous* pair of socks go well with or clash with a suit? _____

4. If someone went through an *ordeal*, would the person be relaxed or stressed out? _____

5. When a student wants to *excel*, does he or she study hard or slack off? _____

6. If Anna is *immersed* in her book, is she interested in what she is reading or bored? _____

Exercise B: Matching

Write the letter of the synonym that matches each vocabulary word.

___ **1.** trivial   **A.** shelter
___ **2.** asylum   **B.** succeed
___ **3.** immersed   **C.** mismatched
___ **4.** struggle   **D.** involved
___ **5.** incongruous   **E.** hard work
___ **6.** excel   **F.** unimportant

UNIT 8

Lesson 1: Word Webs

A **word web** is a kind of chart. It's a quick way to put down your thoughts without worrying about grammar and punctuation. Just let your mind make connections and jot them down. Draw lines between words to show connections.

A word web can be very simple. The synonym web shown here is one word—*read*—with synonyms clustered around it.

```
        Scan        See        Decipher

Skim ———(       Read       )——— Learn

      Interpret    Study      Recognize
```

A word web can be very complicated. The word-association web shown here includes words for people, things, feelings, and other words associated with the theater.

People
- Actors
- Ushers
- Audience
- Stage crew

Things
- Stage
- Seats
- Curtain
- Costumes

(**Theater**)

Feelings
- Joy
- Sadness
- Excitement
- Anticipation

Other Words
- Lights
- Comedy
- Tragedy
- Encore
- Applause

Exercise

Work with a small group to make a word-association web for *summer vacation*. Be sure to include important people, places, feelings, and other words that come to mind as you think of summer vacation.

Lesson 2: Base Words

If someone speaks in an *accusatory* tone, what is that person doing? If you don't know what *accusatory* means, how can you figure it out? The base word *(accuse)* might be a familiar word that can help you guess at the meaning. A base word can stand alone or it can be the basis of other words. Suffixes or prefixes or both can be attached to a base word to make new words.

Prefixes often change the meaning of a word, as when *applicable* ("able to be applied") becomes *inapplicable* ("not able to be applied"). Suffixes, on the other hand, often just change the part of speech, as when *apply* (verb) becomes *applicable* (adjective). An exception to this is *–less*; clearly, *hope* and *hopeless* have very different meanings.

The spelling of the end of a base word often changes when a suffix is added. The *e* in *suppose* changes to an *i* to make *supposition*. Even so, base words are usually obvious if you look for them.

If you come across an unfamiliar word, look at it carefully to see if it has a base word you know. A familiar base word can help you understand a new word.

Exercise A

Write the base word from which each word below was formed. (Remember that a vowel at the end of a base word may change or disappear when a suffix is added.)

1. punster _____   **7.** accredited _____

2. begrime _____   **8.** pressurized _____

3. finery _____   **9.** generation _____

4. presuppose _____   **10.** habitual _____

5. celebratory _____   **11.** solidify _____

6. finality _____   **12.** disembodied _____

Lesson 2: Base Words (continued)

Exercise B

Use your knowledge of the base words and familiar prefixes and suffixes in the underlined words to complete the statements. Circle the letter of the correct answer.

1. If Katie has a feeling of <u>disquietude</u>, she is feeling

   A. relieved   **B.** tired   **C.** upset

2. If a phone call is <u>prophetic</u>, it is one that tells about

   A. danger   **B.** the future   **C.** the past

3. If an event of the past is <u>irreversible</u>, it is one that cannot be

   A. remembered   **B.** changed   **C.** known

4. If a fear is <u>inexpressible</u>, it is one that cannot be

   A. said   **B.** explained   **C.** relieved

5. If June <u>presupposes</u> what happens in a movie, she

   A. sees and hears

   B. remembers

   C. assumes beforehand

6. If the judge gives the lawyer <u>cautionary</u> advice, it is meant to

   A. warn her

   B. encourage her

   C. inform her

7. If Katie <u>theorizes</u> about who has called, it means that she is

   A. guessing who it was

   B. describing the voice

   C. becoming frightened

8. If Corrine becomes <u>uncustomarily</u> silent, it means that her silence is

   A. rude

   B. forced on her

   C. unusual for her

Lesson 3: Roots

A word's **root** is its basic part. It carries the meaning of the word and can usually be used to make other words. For example, the root of *careless* is *care*. Prefixes and suffixes can be added to *care* to get careful, uncaring, and carefree.

Some roots come from Anglo-Saxon—for example, *amaze*, *dear*, *drink*, *knob*, *spell*, *spin*, and *tease*. Even with prefixes and suffixes added to them, you can usually recognize and understand words with these roots. Some words with Greek or Latin roots, however, may be more difficult to interpret. For example, the Latin root *vers*, meaning "to turn," is the basis of the words *reverse* and *versatile*.

If you know the meaning of a root, you may notice it in an unfamiliar word and be able to get some idea of the word's meaning. The chart here shows some common Latin roots.

Root	Meaning	Example
anim	life	animal
aud	hear	auditorium
belli	war	rebellion

Root	Meaning	Example
cogn	know	recognize
cred	believe	credit
dom	house	domestic

Exercise A

Use the chart above as well as your own knowledge to complete each sentence.

1. If the man is not <u>cognizant</u> of the story, he does not

   A. fear it   **B.** know about it   **C.** feel annoyed by it

2. If a thing is <u>audible</u>, it can be

   A. seen   **B.** felt   **C.** heard

3. Stones are <u>inanimate</u> objects, so they must be

   A. hard   **B.** not alive   **C.** not valuable

4. If a man runs away from his <u>domicile</u>, he leaves his

   A. field   **B.** home   **C.** helpers

5. If he tells his story to a <u>credulous</u> listener, the listener is

   A. dishonest   **B.** funny   **C.** believing

6. If soldiers <u>rebel</u>, they will

   A. celebrate   **B.** continue fighting   **C.** disobey their leader

Lesson 3: Roots (continued)

Exercise B

English has developed by borrowing roots, or basic word parts, from other languages. The same root may appear in many different English words. For example, *chronos* is a Greek word that means "time." In English, *chron* is a root from which several words are made that have something to do with time. *Chronic* means "constant, lasting a long time" or "returning repeatedly." So, a *chronic* problem keeps occurring; a *chronic* liar lies frequently.

Complete each item below.

1. Write three months of the year in <u>chronological</u> order.

   _____

2. What do people do when they <u>synchronize</u> their watches? (Hint: The prefix *syn-* means "together.")

   _____

3. Which mistake in a carelessly made movie is an <u>anachronism</u>?
   A. A brontosaurus eats an animal.
   B. A brown dog runs after a ball, but a black dog brings it back.
   C. A motorboat passes by the pilgrims landing at Plymouth Rock.

Exercise C

If you describe something *vividly*, you provide such a clear picture of it that you bring it to life. The word *vivo* in Latin means "live," and *vita* means "life." *Viv* and *vit* are roots, or basic word parts, that have to do with life or liveliness.

Use what you know about the roots *viv* and *vit* to answer each question.

1. How might a <u>vivacious</u> person behave?

   _____

2. Name one <u>vital</u> need that people have.

   _____

3. Who needs to be <u>revived</u>?

   _____

Lesson 4: Suffixes

A **suffix** is a word part added to the end of a base word or a root. Adding a suffix changes the meaning of the word. Sometimes that change is small. A *foolish* person is one who is like a *fool*. Other times the change is major. A *joyless* task is completely without *joy*.

The spelling of the end of a base word often changes when a suffix is added. The *y* in *happy* changes to an *i* to make *happiness*. If you come across an unfamiliar word, look at it carefully to see if it has a suffix and a base word or root that you know. When in doubt, look in a dictionary. The chart below shows a few common suffixes.

Suffix	Meaning	Example	Meaning
–al, –ly, –y	"in the manner of" or "having to do with"	magical hungry	"having to do with magic" "having to do with hunger"
–ee, –eer, –er, –ian, –ist, –or	"one who does"	baker musician debtor clarinetist	"one who bakes" "one who makes music" "one who owes a debt" "one who plays clarinet"
–ful, –ous	"full of"	thankful wondrous	"full of thanks" "full of wonder"

Exercise A

Add a suffix to each underlined base word. Write the new word on the blank and circle the suffix.

1. having to do with <u>dirt</u> _____

2. in the manner of being <u>angry</u> _____

3. one who <u>drives</u> a car _____

4. having to do with the <u>sun</u> _____

5. one who <u>invests</u> money _____

6. full of <u>play</u> _____

7. one who <u>plays</u> _____

8. in the manner of being <u>excited</u> _____

9. full of <u>courage</u> _____

10. having to do with <u>music</u> _____

Leveled Vocabulary Development, ELL

Lesson 4: Suffixes (continued)

Exercise B: The Suffix *–ous*

The suffix *–ous* means "having, full of, or characterized by."
Adding it to a noun creates an adjective. So land that has *mountains*
is *mountainous*. If the noun ends with an *e*, the *e* disappears. So a
day of *adventure* is *adventurous*. If the noun ends with a *y*, the *y*
may change to an *i* or an *e*. Glory becomes *glorious*, "full of glory."
Sometimes the *y* just disappears, as when *treachery* becomes
treacherous.

Match each word on the left to its meaning on the right.

____ **1.** plenteous   **A.** big and empty

____ **2.** torturous   **B.** smelly

____ **3.** cavernous   **C.** more than enough

____ **4.** traitorous   **D.** not trustworthy

____ **5.** odorous   **E.** causing great pain

Exercise C: The Suffix *–ity*

It is *absurd* to try to fill up a house with acorns. The *absurdity* of the
situation would make you laugh. The suffix *–ity* doesn't change the
basic meaning of *absurd*; it makes it into a noun. If you see that two
things are *similar*, you notice a *similarity*. If someone uses *profane*
language, what he or she says is *profanity*. (A word that ends with
a vowel, such as *profane*, usually drops the vowel when *–ity* is
added.)

Use what you know about familiar words and the suffix *–ity* to
match each word to its definition.

____ **1.** totality   **A.** the quality of flowing

____ **2.** solidity   **B.** seriousness or strictness

____ **3.** severity   **C.** hardness or firmness

____ **4.** rarity   **D.** something that is whole or complete

____ **5.** liquidity   **E.** something that is uncommon

Lesson 5: Prefixes

A **prefix** is a word part that can be added to the beginning of a base word or a root. Adding a prefix changes the meaning of the word—a little or a lot. To coexist is to exist along with someone or something else. A *dishonest* person is not honest. The chart below shows a few common prefixes.

Prefix	Meaning	Example	Meaning
co-	"with"	copilot	"one who flies the plane along with the pilot"
dis-, il-, im-, in-, ir-, non-, un-	"not" or "opposite of"	disable illogical impolite nonprofit unwrapped	"not able" "not logical" "not polite" "not for profit" "not wrapped"
post-	"after"	postwar	"after the war"
pre-	"before"	pre-approved	"approved in advance"
sub-	"below" or "beneath"	sublevel	"below the level"

Exercise A

Add a prefix to the underlined base word to build a new word that matches the definition.

1. beneath a <u>category</u> _____

2. not <u>regular</u> _____

3. opposite of <u>satisfactory</u> _____

4. not <u>active</u> _____

5. to <u>sign</u> together _____

6. <u>folded</u> beforehand _____

7. after the <u>election</u> _____

8. opposite of <u>sense</u> _____

9. <u>arranged</u> ahead of time _____

Lesson 5: Prefixes (continued)

Exercise B

The prefixes *il-*, *im-*, *in-*, and *ir-* add a negative meaning to many words. For example, *impatience* means "without patience," and *illegal* is the opposite of *legal*. However, these prefixes don't always add a negative meaning. An *intense* person is not calm. You don't *improve* something by showing it to be false. When in doubt, look up the word in a dictionary.

All of the words below begin with *il-*, *im-*, *in-*, or *ir-*. However, in some of the words, the prefix does NOT have a negative meaning. Circle the TWO words in each set that have a negative prefix.

1. irresponsible   inflate   independent

2. introduce   incapable   irregular

3. inconvenient   insincere   irritate

Exercise C: The Prefixes *ex-* and *exo-*

The prefix *ex-* has several meanings, but it usually has to do with "out." An *exit* is where you go out. When you breathe out, you *exhale*. The prefix *exo-* means "outside." *Exotic* (eg ZOT ik) means "strangely beautiful or interesting; unusual." Something that is *exotic* is "outside" of our regular experience, and that's why foreign countries and customs are often described as *exotic*.

Use what you know about familiar words and the prefixes *ex-* and *exo-* to answer the following questions.

1. You know what *include* means, so what does it mean to <u>exclude</u> someone from a club? _____

2. You know that a *tractor* is a machine for pulling, so what does a dentist do to a tooth by <u>extracting</u> it? _____

3. You know what a *skeleton* is, so which animal has an <u>exoskeleton</u>—a dog, a clam, or a bird? _____

Lesson 6: Context Clues

What do you think *obdurate* means in the following sentence?

> Some people react in an obdurate way to certain situations but not to others.

The sentence provides no clues about the meaning of *obdurate*, except that the word is an adjective. Sometimes you can find information about an unfamiliar word by looking at its context, the sentence or paragraph in which the word appears. The context often provides **context clues** that help readers figure out what an unfamiliar word means.

There are many kinds of context clues, and the amount of help they provide varies. Study the examples below.

- Our <u>obdurate</u> boss insisted that we finish the job on time, even though we were missing half our workers.

This example provides only a little help. Being *obdurate* doesn't seem to be such a good thing, but what does it mean?

- A stubborn person may become more <u>obdurate</u> if nagged.

This example has a couple of context clues. The words *stubborn* and *more* make it clear that *stubborn* and obdurate are synonyms.

- Lisa was too <u>obdurate</u> to follow the coach's suggestions.

Lisa won't follow the advice of her coach, a more experienced person. She must be stubborn in a determined way.

- It's hard to reason with an <u>obdurate</u> person—someone who simply won't give in.

This example provides a definition.

Exercise A

Use context clues to figure out what the underlined words mean. Write a synonym or a short definition for each word.

1. That wall is sure to topple over without a <u>buttress</u>, that is, support.

_____

2. Students must read the complete novel, not an <u>abridgment</u>.

_____

Lesson 6: Context Clues (continued)

3. Jackie is afraid her home-made dress will look ugly or tacky, but she's surprised at how <u>sophisticated</u> it looks.

_____

4. In Korea, people follow rules of <u>reverence</u> and use titles of respect when they speak to others.

_____

5. The stranger seemed to be a <u>menacing</u> figure at first, but he was a harmless old man who just wanted to protect his few belongings.

_____

6. Don't just <u>jabber</u>! Speak slowly and give some thought to what you are saying.

_____

7. How could Stan go sailing? He doesn't know a <u>jib</u> from a mainsail!

_____

8. Hospital volunteers wheel patients from place to place on <u>gurneys</u>.

_____

9. The <u>acoustics</u> of this hall are wonderful for a symphony orchestra—the softest sounds carry clearly to the last row of seats.

_____

Exercise B
Read each sentence. Use context clues to figure out the meaning of the underlined word. Then circle the letter before the definition that makes sense in the sentence.

1. Fortunately, the <u>machinations</u> of the enemy were so clumsy that the king discovered the conspiracy before it could harm him.

   A. plots   **B.** inventions

2. The villain was so <u>malevolent</u> in the first part of the movie that his last-minute change to being good and kind was hard to believe.

   A hard to see   **B.** full of evil

3. Without the <u>linchpin</u> of a strong leader, the movement will never succeed.

   A. type of safety pin   **B.** central element holding something together

Lesson 7: Homographs

George Washington was one of the *founders* of the nation. A horse that *founders* stumbles or goes lame. A ship that *founders* fills up with water and sinks. These are **homographs**—different words with the same spelling. Some homographs, such as *founder*, look and sound the same. Others can look the same but be pronounced differently.

How can a reader tell which meaning for a word is the right one? The best clues are found in the sentence or paragraph the word is in. If you read that "the scene was *arresting*," it must be a view that stops you and demands your attention; it doesn't involve the police.

You might read a sentence and think you understand all the words, but the sentence doesn't make sense. For example, you might read about "a bank of elevators." You may be confused if you think that a *bank* has to be (a) a place for keeping money or (b) the land along a river. If you know that a *bank* can also be (c) a row of objects, it makes sense. How can you tell what meaning is right? The best clues are found in the sentence the word is in.

Exercise A

Look at the definition for each word. Then circle the letter of the sentence that uses a *different* meaning for that word.

1. *fresh: rude, sassy*
   A. We need some <u>fresh</u> ideas.
   B. <u>Fresh</u> remarks will get you in trouble.

2. *graze: to feed on grass*
   A. The horse <u>grazed</u> all afternoon in the pasture.
   B. The horse just <u>grazed</u> me as he galloped past.

Exercise B

Match each underlined word with its definition.

___ **1.** a <u>cutting</u> remark   **A.** mastery
___ **2.** a <u>pocket</u> of ignorance   **B.** small area
___ **3.** a <u>command</u> of French   **C.** meant to hurt
___ **4.** on the <u>scent</u> of the thief **D.** trail of clues

Lesson 8: Homophones

The word *homophone* comes from *homo*, meaning "same," and *phone*, meaning "sound." Therefore, **homophones** are words that sound the same. However, homophones have different meanings and spellings. For example, to *pedal* a bike is to ride it; to *peddle* a bike is to try to sell it. Not recognizing a homophone can result in spelling errors. Even a computer can't fix your mistake if you wrote *flower* when you should have written *flour*, because both of those words are spelled correctly.

The English language includes many homophones. A baby antelope is a *new gnu*. If you've watched a short play, you have *seen* a *scene*. Some homophones are only slightly different in meaning, such as *who's* and *whose*, and you might have to give some thought to choosing the correct one. Usually, however, using the wrong homophone is simply a result of being careless.

Exercise A

Work alone or with a partner to write two sentences that use homophone pairs. Make your sentences similar to the ones about the antelope and the play. (To help you get started, complete this sentence: A cake that a female servant baked is one that a ...)

Exercise B

If the underlined word is correct, write **C**. If it is a homophone for the correct word, write the word that should be used.

The soldiers were not **(1)** week; they were young. Death awaited many at the **(2)** break of day, soon after the **(3)** sun **(4)** rows in the sky. The general **(5)** new that training could **(6)** lesson the hardships his men **(7)** would face, but **(8)** their was no time for that. All he could **(9)** due was **(10)** to walk among them and speak to them.

1. _____   6. _____
2. _____   7. _____
3. _____   8. _____
4. _____   9. _____
5. _____   10. _____

Lesson 9: Idioms

A word or phrase that has a meaning other than its literal meaning is an **idiom**. Saying that a *dog* is <u>tied up</u> in the backyard probably means that the dog is literally tied up. But saying that a *person* is <u>tied up</u> in the backyard probably means that the person is busy there. Some idioms, such as "Get off my back," and "Cut it out!" are familiar. Unfamiliar idioms, however, can cause confusion. One way to figure out the meaning of an unfamiliar idiom is to think about what the ordinary meanings of the words suggest.

> Naomi attended a lecture about the swallowtail butterfly. The talk was <u>over her head</u>, but she liked it.

If something were literally over Naomi's head, it would be above her and hard to reach. In this case, the talk was beyond the reach of her understanding.

> Nigel doesn't want to make any plans for Saturday. He's just going to wait and <u>play it by ear</u>.

According to the context clues, making plans and "playing it by ear" are two very different things. "Playing it by ear" is what you do when you don't make plans. The clues suggest that when people "play it by ear," they decide what to do as they go along.

Exercise A
Circle the letter of the phrase that will correctly finish the sentence.

1. If something will happen <u>come rain or shine</u>, it will happen

   A. at some point   **C.** no matter what

   B. outside   **D.** depending on the weather

2. If your plans are <u>up in the air</u>, they are

   A. undecided   **C.** floating

   B. unimportant   **D.** silly

3. When you <u>jump on the bandwagon</u>, you

   A. take a rest   **C.** join in with the crowd

   B. take a ride   **D.** continue what you were doing

Lesson 9: Idioms (continued)

4. When you <u>put the cart before the horse</u>, you

   A. know how to care for horses

   B. do things in the wrong order

   C. can't do something

   D. plan ahead

Exercise B

Match the sentences that have the same meaning. Write the letters
of your choices on the lines.

____ **1.** You have to learn it by heart.   **A.** You look sad.

____ **2.** You have a long face.   **B.** You have to memorize it.

____ **3.** You are a chip off the old block.   **C.** You have to take what's coming.

____ **4.** You have to start from scratch.   **D.** You are like your father.

____ **5.** You have to face the music.   **E.** You have to start at the beginning.

Exercise C

Rewrite these sentences, using your own words to replace the
underlined idioms.

1. I am a good fielder, but I hit home runs <u>once in a blue moon</u>.

_____

2. Thanks to our advance planning, the job should <u>run like
clockwork</u>.

_____

3. I am tired of listening to your <u>half-baked</u> ideas.

_____

4. Don't <u>jump down my throat</u> just because I made one mistake.

_____

5. Alia's report described our city's recycling program <u>in a
nutshell</u>.

_____

Lesson 10: Dictionary Pronunciations

Does *gauge* sound like *page* or like *garage*? Pronouncing an unfamiliar word can be tricky, because vowels and some consonants, like *g* and *c*, have more than one pronunciation. When in doubt, check a dictionary for the correct pronunciation shown with letters and symbols. *Gauge* appears like this: gāj. The first *g* has the "hard" *g* sound; the second one has the "soft" *g* sound—the same sound that *j* has. In between, there is the sound of a long *a*. So *gauge* rhymes with *page*.

In a dictionary pronunciation, a vowel with no symbol has a "short" sound, like the vowels in *bat, bet, bit, blot,* and *but*. Other vowel sounds are shown by symbols, such as a straight line above the vowel to show that it is a long vowel. An accent mark points to the syllable you should stress. Stressing the correct syllable is extremely important. For example, the only difference in the sounds of *dessert* and *desert* is which syllable is stressed.

ä	the **ah** sound in *father*
ô	the **aw** sound in *coffee* and *law*
oo	the vowel sound in *wood* and *could*
o͞o	the vowel sound in *fool*
oi	the vowel sound in *toy*
ou	the **ow** sound in *cow* and *out*
ə	the unaccented vowel sound in *pencil, lemon,* and *taken*

Exercise A

Using the pronunciation given, circle the correct answer.

1. Which rhymes with *aghast* (ə gast′)? *fast waste*

2. Which rhymes with *psyche* (sī′ kē)? *like spiky itchy rich*

3. Which rhymes with the first syllable of *scavenger* (skav′ in jər)? *have save*

Exercise B

Circle the word that is represented by each dictionary pronunciation.

1. (ān′ jəl) *angle* (corner) *angel* (heavenly being)

2. (buk′ it) *bucket* *bouquet*

3. (pos′ ēz) *possess* *posse's*

Answer Key
Course 3, Unit 1, ELL

Ice

Exercise A: True or False?

1. F
2. T
3. F
4. T
5. F

Exercise B: Context Clues

1. characteristic
2. slipped through the detective's hands
3. only, small
4. stubbornly, until it was done
5. did not notice

On Top of the World

Exercise A: Words in Context

1. coworkers
2. short
3. top
4. quickly
5. did

Exercise B: Answer Questions

1. proud
2. walk
3. dangerous
4. travel
5. win

The Tell-Tale Heart, Part A

Exercise A: Word Groups

1. bored
2. missed
3. shyness
4. discourages
5. real

Exercise B: Context Clues

1. C
2. I
3. C
4. I
5. C

The Tell-Tale Heart, Part B

Exercise: Crossword Puzzle

DOWN

2. inquiring
3. pitied
4. stalked
5. thrust
7. ceased

ACROSS

1. triumph
4. sufficient
8. awe
9. hearty
10. resolved

from The Book of Rock Stars

Exercise A: Context Clues

1. chosen
2. fight against
3. concern
4. chase after
5. not able to improve

Exercise B: Words in Context

1. devotion
2. comeback
3. hypnotic
4. premature
5. converted

The March of the Mill Children

Exercise A: This or That?

1. talking quietly
2. talk to
3. mosquitoes
4. stay off
5. very tired
6. ruined

Exercise B: Words in Context

1. weary
2. hesitated
3. grumbled
4. dormitory

Filling Out the Application and Exploring Careers

Exercise A: Mystery Word

1. replacement
2. accurate
3. irregular
4. prone
5. current

Mystery Word: permit

Exercise B: Words in Context

1. requested
2. residences
3. dependable
4. revive

Copyright © by The McGraw-Hill Companies, Inc.

from Akiko in the Forbidden Foothills of Gozmaturk

Exercise A: Words in Context

1. unarmed
2. lullaby
3. heavenly
4. wretched
5. coordinate

Exercise B: Synonyms or Antonyms?

1. S
2. A
3. S
4. A
5. S

Being Japanese American

Exercise A: Matching

1. C
2. D
3. E
4. B
5. A

Exercise B: Analogies

1. object
2. corresponded
3. treasured
4. humiliated
5. branch

from A Gift of Laughter

Exercise A: Synonyms

1. bounded
2. appealed
3. bewilderment
4. rage
5. contributor

Exercise B: Words in Context

1. magnificent
2. superiority
3. shuddering
4. worthy
5. staccato

A Family Thing and Knoxville, Tennessee

Exercise A: Words in Context

1. C
2. C
3. B
4. B
5. C

Exercise B: Matching

1. E
2. C
3. B
4. A
5. D

Course 3, Unit 2, ELL

The People Could Fly

Exercise A: Words in Context

1. ancient
2. snag
3. clumsily
4. soothe
5. captured

Exercise B: Matching

1. C
2. E
3. B
4. A
5. D

A Father's Daring Trek

Exercise A: Words in Context

1. A
2. A
3. C
4. B

Exercise B: Antonyms

1. perilous
2. frigid
3. hardships
4. sacrifice

Paul Revere's Ride

Exercise A: True or False?

1. F
2. F
3. T
4. T
5. F

Exercise B: Context Clues

Answers will vary. Possible responses:

1. quiet, peaceful
2. disrespectful, ran away
3. started the prairie fire
4. came out
5. crept slowly

The Oxcart

Exercise A: Words in Context

1. as a big group
2. jerking
3. important people
4. a bad smell

Exercise B: If . . . ?

1. beautiful
2. ashamed
3. rude
4. a surprise

The Snake Chief

Exercise A: Context Clues

Answers will vary. Possible responses:
1. persuade
2. becoming rich
3. stubborn
4. happily

Exercise B: Complete the Sentence

1. boast
2. incompetence
3. reluctantly
4. courteously
5. quavered
6. induce

from Harriet Tubman: Conductor on the Underground Railroad, Part A

Exercise A: Word Groups

1. allowed
2. hide
3. warning
4. punishment
5. slowly

Exercise B: True or False?

1. T
2. F
3. F

from Harriet Tubman: Conductor on the Underground Railroad, Part B

Exercise A: Crack the Code

1. disheveled
2. defeated
3. vicinity
4. fugitives
5. indicate
6. whence
7. invariably
8. suspicious

Password: "A friend with friends."

Icarus and Daedalus

Exercise A: Mystery Word

1. captive
2. rash
3. offering
4. quench
5. cunning
6. vacancy

Mystery word: cautions

Exercise B: Complete the Conversation

1. veered
2. rash
3. wavered
4. remained
5. quench

A Dose of Medicine

Exercise A: This or That?

1. might have
2. turning it down
3. asleep
4. talked about
5. give the shot

Exercise B: Words in Context

1. stagger
2. collapsed
3. extracted
4. eager
5. hilarious

Kamau's Finish

Exercise A: Words in Context

1. prodded/distracted
2. scold/financial
3. crouch/sheepishly
4. dramatic/beaming
5. destination/jolts

Exercise B: Synonyms or Antonyms?

1. A
2. A
3. S

The Bunion Derby

Exercise A: Matching

1. B
2. D
3. A
4. C

Exercise B: Answer Questions

1. furnished
2. doggedly
3. grimacing
4. consecutive

Course 3, Unit 3, ELL

Gymnasts in Pain: Out of Balance, Part A

Exercise A: Context Clues

1. sneaking
2. top
3. skilled
4. passion
5. pushing

Exercise B: Words in Context

Answers will vary. Possible answers:

1. downplayed
2. fragile
3. scorn
4. expectations
5. decade

Gymnasts in Pain: Out of Balance, Part B

Exercise: Word Search

1. sensation
2. verbal
3. consuming
4. inserted
5. repeatedly
6. recalled
7. daring
8. similar
9. fractured
10. acknowledged

In Response to Executive Order 9066

Exercise A: Words in Context

1. C
2. B
3. A
4. A
5. C

Exercise B: Context Clues

1. C
2. C
3. C
4. I
5. C

The Games Kids Play

Exercise A: Mystery Word

1. modified
2. transformed
3. aggression
4. clamor

Mystery Word: declines

Exercise B: Synonyms or Antonyms?

1. S
2. A
3. S
4. A
5. S
6. S
7. A
8. S

Cruise Control

Exercise A: Words in Context

1. beloved
2. humiliating
3. banners
4. restrictions
5. notify

Exercise B: Synonyms

1. restrictions
2. banners
3. beloved
4. perceives
5. humiliating

Exercise C: Responding to the Selection

Answers will vary.

Flowers for Algernon, Part 2, Part A

Exercise A: Matching

1. B
2. E
3. C
4. A
5. D

Exercise B: Context Clues

1. no coincidence
2. each and every time
3. found the pages stuck togther with peanut butter
4. fearfully in a corner
5. did not react

Flowers for Algernon, Part 2, Part B

Exercise: Crossword Puzzle

DOWN

1. impaired
2. significant
3. despised
4. disturbed
6. smirking
7. incident

ACROSS

5. accomplishing
8. equipped
9. toying
10. technique

Tattoos: Fad, Fashion, or Folly?

Exercise A: True or False?

1. T
2. T
3. F
4. F
5. T

Exercise B: Words in Context

1. implements
2. pigments
3. practiced
4. compiled
5. indelible

Wearing Hijab: Veil of Valor

Exercise A: Mystery Word

1. valor
2. stellar
3. intercede
4. transition
5. clarified

Mystery Word: tolerance

Exercise B: Words in Context

1. decorated with words
2. disapproved
3. stayed quiet
4. liked
5. very important

from Zoya's Story

Exercise A: This or That?

1. uncomfortable
2. rough
3. unhappy
4. fall down

Exercise B: Words in Context

1. instinctively
2. jauntily
3. severed
4. edict
5. perpetrated

Wishing Well

Exercise A: Words in Context

1. unconcerned
2. minerals
3. comforter
4. arc
5. mesh
6. flannel
7. dull

Exercise B: Complete the Paragraph

1. arc
2. minerals
3. dull
4. unconcerned
5. mesh

Mother to Son *and* Harlem

Exercise A: Multiple Choice

1. B
2. C
3. C
4. A
5. B

Exercise B: Context Clues

1. C
2. C
3. I
4. I
5. I

Exercise C: Responding to the Selection

Answers will vary.

Sittin' on the Dock of the Bay

Exercise A: Matching

1. E
2. D
3. B
4. C
5. A

Exercise B: Words in Context

1. bay
2. dock
3. remains
4. roamed
5. tide

Exercise C: Responding to the Selection

Answers will vary.

from To the Democratic National Convention

Exercise A: Context Clues

1. vultures, deer lying on the road
2. radio, of the game, FM102
3. for class president
4. bankrupt, money
5. doctor, assist, accident victims

Exercise B: Synonyms or Antonyms?

1. A
2. S
3. A
4. S
5. S

Fable for When There's No Way Out

Exercise A: Words in Context

1. rage
2. despair
3. tomb
4. instinct
5. ambition

Exercise B: Context Clues

1. I
2. C
3. I
4. C
5. C

O Captain! My Captain!

Exercise A: Matching

1. B
2. G
3. E
4. F
5. A
6. C
7. D

Exercise B: Context Clues

1. made up of daisies, miniature roses
2. fifty-pound weight, boat, going nowhere
3. shook her opponent's hand, joyful grin
4. lonely, missing family
5. moved from side to side

Scorched! How to Handle Different Types of Burns, Part A

Exercise A: Words in Context

1. with difficulty
2. a fire
3. cover a wound
4. dirty
5. heal an injury

Exercise B: This or That?

1. overcooked
2. spotty
3. make a hole
4. at risk of getting sick
5. a blanket

Scorched! How to Handle Different Types of Burns, Part B

Exercise A: Crossword Puzzle

ACROSS

3. severity
5. assistance
9. underlying
10. resuscitation

DOWN

1. reduce
2. ointment
4. minor
6. sustaining
7. oozing
8. bacteria

from Thura's Diary

Exercise A: True or False?

1. F
2. T
3. T
4. F
5. F

Exercise B: Words in Context

1. freak
2. wilt
3. circumstances
4. precious
5. rations

Exercise C: Responding to the Selection

Answers will vary.

Escaping

Exercise A: Word Groups

1. hopelessness
2. handed over
3. friendly
4. helped
5. restricted
6. unimportant
7. failed
8. unawareness

Exercise B: Answer Questions

1. imperative
2. glistened
3. succeeded
4. realization
5. infested

Course 3, Unit 5, ELL

Cream Puff

Exercise A: True or False?

1. T
2. F
3. T
4. F
5. F

Exercise B: Which Word?

1. rattled
2. slunk
3. caressing
4. swaggered
5. confirmed
6. sneering

The Question of Popularity

Exercise A: Finding Synonyms

1. sweet
2. careers
3. invite
4. outcast
5. outcome

Exercise B: Words in Context

1. envied
2. insecurity
3. acceptance
4. varies
5. majority

an african american

Exercise A: Matching Definitions

1. anthem
2. barriers
3. unison
4. spiritual

Exercise B: Complete the Paragraph

1. desperately
2. mimicked
3. continent
4. ancestors
5. croons

One Throw

Exercise A: This or That?

1. ten seconds
2. familiar
3. first floor
4. encouraging her
5. smiling

Exercise B: Words in Context

1. recognize
2. exaggerating
3. sore
4. bawls
5. needle

The Medicine Bag

Exercise A: Complete the Sentence

1. glamorous
2. stately
3. commotion
4. fatigue
5. rumpled

Exercise B: Context Clues

1. I
2. C
3. I
4. I
5. C

A Year of Living Bravely

Exercise A: Matching

1. E
2. C
3. B
4. A
5. D

Exercise B: If . . . ?

1. be scared of it
2. shy
3. forgive her
4. finish reading it

The Fire Pond, Part A

Exercise A: True or False?

1. F
2. T
3. T
4. T
5. F

Exercise B: Synonyms or Antonyms?

1. A
2. S
3. A
4. S
5. A

The Fire Pond, Part B

Exercise A: Word Search

1. rally
2. sheer
3. seeps
4. trudge
5. trample
6. stationed
7. embers
8. blaring
9. darting
10. spooked

from Savion!: My Life in Tap

Exercise A: Using Synonyms

1. bunched up
2. healthy
3. ease around them
4. humiliating loss

Exercise B: Context Clues

1. I
2. C
3. I
4. C

A Retrieved Reformation (Henry)

Exercise A: Matching Synonyms

1. scarce
2. discharged
3. sociable
4. compulsory
5. escorted

Exercise B: Complete the Conversation

1. simultaneously
2. alibi
3. duplicate
4. retribution
5. venture

A Retrieved Reformation (Gianni)

Exercise A: Words in Context

1. disregarding
2. boarded
3. fondly
4. clemency
5. eminent

Exercise B: Matching Synonyms

1. C
2. A
3. E
4. B
5. D

Course 3, Unit 6, ELL

The Diary of Anne Frank, Act 1, Scene 3

Exercise A: Words in Context

1. absurd
2. meticulous
3. bickering
4. self-conscious
5. dignified

Exercise B: True or False

1. F
2. F
3. T
4. F
5. T

The Diary of Anne Frank, Act 1, Scenes 4–5, Part A

Exercise A: Complete the Diary Entry

1. clinging
2. accustomed
3. improvised
4. audible
5. gradually
6. dim
7. appalled
8. strain
9. hesitates
10. weather

The Diary of Anne Frank, Act 1, Scenes 4–5, Part B

Exercise A: Matching

1. D
2. C
3. E
4. A
5. B

Exercise B: Words in Context
1. makeshift
2. bearings
3. wallow
4. sustenance
5. hysterically

The Diary of Anne Frank, Act 2, Scenes 1–2

Exercise A: Words in Context
1. worried
2. were not
3. sensed
4. calmly
5. take advantage of

Exercise B: This or That?
1. stopped
2. worried
3. grouchy
4. better

The Diary of Anne Frank, Act 2, Scenes 3–5 , Part A

Exercise: Crossword Puzzle

ACROSS
1. post
4. whimper
5. obligation
8. bitterness
10. remorse

DOWN
2. succession
3. bewildered
6. insistent
7. abruptly
9. frenzy

The Diary of Anne Frank, Act 2, Scenes 3–5, Part B

Exercise A: True or False
1. T
2. T
3. F
4. T
5. F

Exercise B: Context Clues
1. fidget, chewing her fingernails
2. crept
3. angry
4. stormed
5. climbed the goalposts

Bouncing Back *and* Another Mountain

Exercise A: Context Clues
Answers will vary. Possible responses:
1. first plan
2. brief
3. next stage
4. poor
5. ideal spot, lookout tower

Exercise B: Sentence Completion
Answers will vary. Possible responses:
1. it leaves the audience hanging
2. study even harder
3. break it down into small steps
4. giving them good advice
5. put it off until the last minute

Standing Tall

Exercise A: Mystery Word
1. withstand
2. tribute
3. stable
4. shatter
5. collapse
Mystery word: enable

Exercise B: Context Clues
1. C
2. C
3. C
4. I
5. I
6. I

from Sky

Exercise A: Words Groups
1. silly
2. real
3. staying
4. action-packed
5. welcomed

Exercise B: Words in Context
1. amiss
2. observant
3. grave
4. precautions
5. anticipation

Exercise A: Words in Context

1. hazy
2. souvenir
3. ultimatum
4. dismal
5. pivoted

Exercise B: Synonyms or Antonyms?

1. S
2. A
3. A
4. S
5. S

Exercise C: Responding to the Selection

Answers will vary.

Course 3, Unit 7, ELL

Saving Water: Why Save Something That Covers Two-thirds of the Earth?

Exercise A: Words in Context

1. vast
2. fixed
3. distribution
4. approximately
5. rushing

Exercise B: Matching

1. C
2. D
3. B
4. E
5. A

Exercise C: Responding to the Selection

Answers will vary.

from The Measure of Our Success

Exercise A: This or That?

1. keep going
2. notice
3. let it go on
4. not study
5. high

Exercise B: Mystery Word

1. entitled
2. persistence
3. corruption
4. upbringing
5. racial

Mystery word: respond

Exercise A: Complete the Sentence

1. C
2. C
3. B
4. C
5. A

Exercise B: Context Clues

1. C
2. I
3. C
4. C

from Through My Eyes

Exercise A: Matching

1. E
2. C
3. D
4. B
5. A

Exercise B: Complete the Sentence

1. assemble
2. Barricades
3. clustered
4. gripped
5. taunts

Exercise C: Responding to the Selection

Answers will vary.

The Trouble with Television, Part A

Exercise A: Fill in the Boxes

1. enhances
2. skeptically
3. gratification
4. strain

Exercise B: Synonyms or Antonyms?

1. S
2. A
3. A
4. S
5. S

Exercise C: Responding to the Selection

Answers will vary.

The Trouble with Television, Part B

Exercise A: MacNeil's Bumper Sticker

1. constructive
2. inefficient
3. simplistic
4. dominating
5. resolutions
6. earnest

Bumper sticker: SELL YOUR TELEVISION!!!

Exercise B: Responding to the Selection

Answers will vary.

Teen Curfews

Exercise A: Words in Context

1. aced
2. controversial
3. violating
4. convictions
5. curbing

Exercise B: Context Clues

1. C
2. I
3. C
4. I
5. C

Rally for Better Food

Exercise A: Matching

1. E
2. D
3. A
4. C
5. B

Exercise B: Context Clues

1. hundreds of people, to protest
2. refused to ride the bus
3. fooled, fake diploma
4. walked into the restaurant
5. provided ten essential vitamins and minerals

Exercise C: Responding to the Selection

Answers will vary.

Stop the Sun

Exercise A: Words in Context

1. inert
2. squirming
3. ruin
4. blurted
5. syndrome
6. dry
7. browsed

Exercise B: If . . . ?

1. graceless
2. innocent
3. unexciting
4. upset
5. without a purpose

Teens Tackle Pollution in Their Communities

Exercise A: True or False?

1. F
2. T
3. T
4. F
5. T

Exercise B: Complete the Sentence

1. testified
2. emit
3. empowered
4. buoyed
5. ultimate

A Change in Climate

Exercise A: Words in Context

1. C
2. B
3. A
4. B
5. C

Exercise B: Word Scramble

1. trends
2. accumulate
3. impact
4. drastic
5. alarming

Volar

Exercise A: Synonyms

1. enthusiastic
2. dream
3. frequent
4. suddenly
5. trash

Exercise B: Context Clues

1. C
2. I
3. C
4. I
5. C

from The Century for Young People

Exercise A: Multiple Choice

1. A
2. C
3. B
4. C
5. A

Exercise B: Complete the Sentence

1. operated
2. literally
3. overwhelmed
4. accumulated
5. admitted

Lottery Winners Who Lost Their Millions

Exercise A: Word Groups

1. joy
2. loss
3. firstly
4. unsure
5. brief

Exercise B: Synonyms or Antonyms?

1. A
2. S
3. S
4. A
5. A

The Gettysburg Address

Exercise A: Words in Context

1. conceived
2. detract
3. advanced
4. devotion
5. vain

Exercise B: Match the Clue

1. proposition
2. to endure
3. task
4. resolve
5. perish

I Chose Schooling

Exercise A: Matching

1. D
2. B
3. A
4. E
5. C

Exercise B: Context Clues

1. desire
2. best experience, gold medal
3. stressed, importance
4. every night at the library, homework
5. pacing restlessly

The Electric Summer

Exercise A: Words in Context

1. first
2. delighted
3. dangerous
4. never
5. annoyed

Exercise B: If . . . ?

1. in the mountains
2. staying in one place
3. less expensive
4. stay

from Dandelion Wine, Part A

Exercise A: True or False?

1. F
2. T
3. F
4. T

Exercise B: Complete the Sentence

1. capsize
2. proprietor
3. flex
4. rave
5. alien

from **Dandelion Wine**, Part B

Exercise: Word Search

1. detached
2. limber
3. vanished
4. seized
5. emporium
6. hushed
7. irritable
8. airy

Coming to America (McGowan)

Exercise A: Mystery Word

1. toiled
2. version
3. rethinking
4. track
5. discriminates

Mystery word: consider

Exercise B: Words in Context

1. just arrived
2. has moved from
3. time
4. hurts

Coming to America (Szegedy-Maszak)

Exercise A: This or That?

1. help her
2. not a big deal
3. clash
4. stressed out
5. study hard
6. interested in

Exercise B: Matching

1. F
2. A
3. D
4. E
5. C
6. B

Course 3, Lessons 1–10, ELL

Lesson 1: Word Webs

Exercise

Answers will vary.

Lesson 2: Base Words

Exercise A

1. pun
2. grime
3. fine
4. suppose
5. celebrate
6. final

7. credit
8. pressure
9. generate
10. habit
11. solid
12. body

Exercise B

1. C
2. B
3. B
4. A
5. C
6. A
7. A
8. C

Lesson 3: Roots

Exercise A

1. B
2. C
3. B
4. B
5. C
6. C

Exercise B

1. *Sample answer:* April, May, June
2. *Sample answer:* set the watches to the same time
3. C

Exercise C

Wording of answers will vary.

1. in a lively way
2. food
3. someone who fainted

Lesson 4: Suffixes

Exercise A

1. dir<u>ty</u>
2. ang<u>rily</u>
3. driv<u>er</u>
4. sun<u>ny</u>
5. invest<u>or</u>
6. play<u>ful</u>
7. play<u>er</u>
8. excited<u>ly</u>
9. courag<u>eous</u>
10. musi<u>cal</u>

Exercise B

1. C
2. E
3. A
4. D
5. B

Exercise C

1. D
2. C
3. B
4. E
5. A

Lesson 5: Prefixes

Exercise A

1. subcategory
2. irregular
3. unsatisfactory
4. inactive
5. co-sign
6. prefolded
7. post-election
8. nonsense
9. prearranged

Exercise B

1. irresponsible, independent
2. incapable, irregular
3. inconvenient, insincere

Exercise C

Wording will vary.

1. leave out
2. pulls it out
3. a clam

Lesson 6: Context Clues

Exercise A

Wording of definitions will vary.

1. something that supports a wall
2. a shortened version
3. beautiful and tasteful
4. honor and respect
5. threatening
6. talk nonsense
7. part of a sailboat
8. beds on wheels
9. sound qualities

Exercise B

1. A
2. B
3. B

Lesson 7: Homographs

Exercise A

1. A
2. B

Exercise B

1. C
2. B
3. A
4. D

Lesson 8: Homophones

Exercise A

A cake that a female servant baked is one that a maid made. Other answers will vary.

Exercise B

1. weak
2. C
3. C
4. rose
5. knew
6. lessen
7. C
8. there
9. do
10. C

Lesson 9: Idioms

Exercise A

1. C
2. A
3. C
4. B

Exercise B

1. B
2. A
3. D
4. E
5. C

Exercise C

Wording of definitions will vary.

1. rarely
2. go smoothly
3. not well thought out
4. get mad at me
5. briefly

Lesson 10: Dictionary Pronunciations

Exercise A

1. fast
2. spiky
3. have

Exercise B

1. angel
2. bucket
3. posse's